Face the Future

Biographical glimpses, jokes, poems and practical advice with Christian devotions about health and wellbeing.

BOOK TWO:

Challenges, joy and faith for Seniors.

William A. M. Cutting

Onwards and Upwards Publishers

Berkeley House, 11 Nightingale Crescent,
Leatherhead, Surrey, KT24 6PD.

www.onwardsandupwards.org

ISBN: 978-1-910197-11-0

Cartoons: Ann Marsden

Cover design: Leah-Maarit

About the Author

William Cutting was born in South India where his father was a medical missionary and his grandfather had been Principal of a Mission High School in Varanasi (Benares, North India). He trained in medicine at Edinburgh University where he met his wife, Margot, who was also training for medical mission work. They worked in rural India, Andhra Pradesh, for twelve years, developing simple child health services and using nutrition rehabilitation to help mothers feed their malnourished children back to health with local foods.

After six years at the London School of Hygiene and Tropical Medicine and the Tropical Child Health Unit of the Institute of Child Health, Great Ormond Street, he was appointed to the Department of Child Life and Health of the University of Edinburgh with special responsibility for international paediatric trainees. He also acted as consultant with WHO, UNICEF, British Council etc. His research interests were wide. At one time he was responsible for two small international teams. In Bangladesh they studied zinc supplementation and catch-up growth in malnourished children, and in Zaire, HIV infection in children. His work provided him much interesting international experience as well as many contacts and friends.

After retiring in 1998, his wide clinical and pastoral interests turned to the many and varied needs of the elderly. He started to collect material, write for and befriend a circle of older people. The paediatrician metamorphosed into a concerned, amateur geriatrician.

Endorsements

This is a book to share with friends, especially Senior friends. The humour, the stories, the illustrations, the practical wisdom, the Bible passages and thoughtful prayers are great to enjoy on one's own, but they would be better enjoyed if read aloud while visiting an old friend. I look forward to doing so with my eldest brother who is in his eighties and living in a Care Home.

Having known William since school days, I know a number of the people who feature in his book, and that has made it specially enjoyable for me. But you don't need to know the people concerned to appreciate what is written about them.

Roger K. Scopes
Retired United Reformed Church minister

Liked the book. Laughed a lot. Send the next ones!

Gerry and Brenda Slavin
Formerly Professors of Histopathology at St. Bartholomew's and of Chemical Pathology at St. Thomas' Medical Colleges, London.
Also worked in Colonial Service Bechuanaland and Al Quds University, Jerusalem.

Laugh-a-lot, amusing and very readable with stories of Seniors and their living experience of the joys and difficulties of living out a faith in Christ. Lots of encouragement and spiritual insights. Sell your shirt to buy this book! A real gem.

Captain Mike Collyer CA
Voluntary Chaplain to Visitors, Sheffield Cathedral, and
    Facilitator of the Seniors' Action Team,
Retired Church Army evangelist and
    trainer in ministry for the elderly

'Face the Future' is a little set of books and a fantastic collection of material. The books are enjoyable, easy to read and just right for that major challenge to our community today: the competent and compassionate care for the elderly.

In God's extended family, in our churches, the older generation are a valued presence with their volunteering, work and loyalty. They have much to offer with their wisdom, skills and experience. But younger adults, children and grandchildren also have much to offer, and these books cross the generations in a light-hearted manner with their stories, cartoons, prayers, wit and wisdom. I strongly commend them to our churches, ministers, deacons and lay workers. Here you will find the inspiration, information and ideas for this growing frontier for ministry.

Dr Daleep Mukarji OBE
Vice President Methodist Church 2013-2014
Director of Christian Aid UK 1998-2010

I enjoyed reading this and hope it will help many. The content is excellent. I would certainly give my mother a copy.

Rev. Julian Hardyman
Senior Pastor, Eden Baptist Church, Cambridge

There is much in Dr William Cutting's highly readable book that will cause pensioners not only to stop and think, but to smile and laugh. He speaks to the heart without bypassing the mind.

Like his first volume of 'Face the Future', this second is a thoughtful and original contribution to the aging process and our mortality. From beginning to end he keeps his readers pondering and laughing.

The book is a lovely blend of seriousness and humour. He once again deals with profound matters lightly and with lighter matters seriously. There is a freshness about the way he explores many of the blessings and joys as well as some of the problems of growing old.

I have long thought that 'Seniors', as William Cutting prefers to call those 'rich in years', are in some respect like house plants; whereas some go to seed, others to pot, others blossom! In this book he highlights some of the secrets of those whose lives not only mature but blossom with the passing years.

The Very Rev. Dr James Simpson
Former Moderator of the General Assembly of the Church of
Scotland, and Minister of Dornoch Cathedral.

Acknowledgements

Dedication – To my family

To the previous generations who nurtured, encouraged, were great role models, servants of God and of their fellow men and women.

To my wife, Margot, who has supported me so faithfully and brought up our children; to my siblings, Christopher, Janet and Elizabeth ('Butter') who in my own generation have served different communities in exemplary ways.

To our children – Alastair, Catriona, Kenneth and Colin – who continue to encourage and inspire me in their varied and devoted roles, and to our grandchildren who show exciting signs of promise.

Thanks – To a host of inspiring Seniors, all of whom I knew personally...

To devout and spirited Senior people in Edinburgh and Surbiton: George Hossack, Robbie Harkness, Betty Forbes, Archie Dale, Tony Davies, Dick Fincham, Connie Hunt and Lionel Wright.

In India: to Rachel Chacko, P. Zachariah, Mollie Smith, Rajamma David, Purushotham Reddy, G.T. Mark, M. Jayanna Joseph, K.C. Mammen, Ann Bothamley, Lesslie Newbigin and also Father Trevor D'Souza of Mumbai, who gave me a copy of 'The Bible for Seniors' and encouraged me to modify and edit William Barclay's Prayers into the booklet 'Prayers for Seniors'.

To professional medical mentors who were inspirational into their advanced years: John Crofton, Denis Burkitt and David Morley.

Thanks – for contributions

In particular to Ann Marsden, a former colleague from India, who has freely given her time and artistic skill to illustrate and enliven a number of articles.

Also I would like to thank the people who have sent me stories, jokes and poems: Chris Cutting, Andrew Griffiths, Ann Eastburgh, Catriona Allen, Liz Colten, Betty Muir, David Bendell, Robert Morley, Norman Allan, Don Harrison, Kier Howard, Robert Schramm and others.

Finally I am very grateful for the guidance and help from Mark and Luke Jeffery, editors at Onwards and Upwards Publishers.

About 'Face the Future'

For many people, old age creeps up on you when you are busy with other things, and very few of us admit to being old. However, "old age is not for wimps"; it brings with it a package of problems that we have to face, live with and adjust to: reduced mobility, failing health, 'forgetfulness', a loss of independence, bereavement and loneliness. But there is much that can be done to *face the future* in a positive manner.

Most Seniors have a heap of things to be thankful for. Many can look back on a wealth of life experiences; many enjoy a degree of security and, by faith in God, can look forward in hope for the big event of old age: death. This is a fact that must not be denied but which, as a Christian, I consider is a new beginning!

The French philosopher, Louis-Vincent Thomas said:

"...only through love, faith and humour can we confront and perhaps transform the terrible realities of old age, decrepitude, and death."[1]

In this series of little books I use this powerful triumvirate of forces to combat what many see as the spectre of old age. Each of these components is important: love, faith and humour. I have woven in many stories and added

---

[1] Louis-Vincent Thomas, quoted by Marie de Hennezel in "The Warmth of the Heart prevents your Body from Rusting", chapter 1 page 13. Published by Rodale, a division of Macmillan, London, 2011.

practical information to help Seniors reduce and deal with some of the physical and social limitations that confront the elderly. Each section is lifted by Ann Marsden's fun pictures, some poems and jokes.

I planned a single volume, but my Editors pointed out that there was too much useful material, that a single volume would be bulky and uncomfortable for the target audience of older people. Smaller volumes would be easier to read and handle. Hence the original book has become a tetralogy.

In **Book One you can find the inspiration, wisdom and faith of many Seniors who are role models for both the elderly and people of any age.**

In Book Two you will see something of the vulnerability of Seniors, but also ways in which being grandparents or having a Christian faith can give great fun and fortitude.

Book Three encourages Seniors to face the future by making the most of the health that they have, by keeping moving and by sensible eating and drinking. There are suggestions about making the best use of the health services.

In Book Four Seniors can consider practical matters like car driving, dental care, facing dementia and preparing to finish well in this life and move on peacefully and positively. It is by no means a gloomy but a hopeful conclusion.

William A.M. Cutting
MBChB (Edin), FRCPE, FRCPCH

Contents

Terminology

What do others call us?
What should we call ourselves?

Older people are sometimes conscious of their limitations, aches and pains, and then we think of ourselves as 'crocks' or 'crumbles'. At times we feel old-fashioned and we think of ourselves as 'dinosaurs', 'fossils' or 'have-beens'. Though aware of our fragility at times, we are not happy about others referring to us by these names, or even as 'the sunset brigade', as if we are on the way out and sinking fast. These things smack of ageism.

Some names have a hint of the promise or even the power of later years such as 'golden oldies' or 'silver surfers' or 'the great grey vote'. There are also gentler and more neutral titles such as 'the older generation' or 'elders' or 'old folk'. But I have chosen to adopt the single word or name 'Seniors'.

It has limitations, as some have pointed out. You can be senior in years but short in worldly wisdom and vice versa. However, 'Seniors' derives something from the widely used term 'senior citizens', which I do not consider to be demeaning. Rather, I like to think it carries a sense of 'responsible and respected in society'. So in these books you will find the word Seniors used throughout.

Foreword by Dr James Woodward

Like many of you reading this book I am thankful for my satellite navigation system. It is one of those advances in technology that has helped us all to move with confidence to our desired destinations. However I regret the loss of maps and have happy memories of holidays in Europe with friends where a map was shared between us. We often turned it around and looked at it from different angles until someone discovered where we were going! On a journey it can be interesting, demanding and sometimes even fun getting lost; we are constantly in the process of finding and re-finding our sense of direction.

If this is true for a geographical journey, perhaps it is also an analogy we can apply to other aspects of our life journey. We shall need some kind of direction, a map, company and sources of information, wisdom and challenge.

I reflected on this journey analogy in my experience of working alongside a vast range of individuals and groups considering and reflecting upon the nature of age. Many fear the possibility of indignity and loss in old age. We wonder what we may become. We might reflect on the relationship between our younger and older selves. On our journey ageing offers us an opportunity: of becoming more fully ourselves; more, and not less, individual. Ageing, at each stage of life, can be actively enriching.

In order for this to happen we need to consider the nature of age and what shape age might take in us. We might think of ourselves like wine connoisseurs laying down bottles that will improve with age; fostering in ourselves spiritual qualities that deepen and enrich over the years. Perhaps those who age best are those who travel lightest, who can let go of some thought patterns which might have been helpful at one stage of life but need discarding when they are ill-suited to another. A certain suppleness of spirit is needed. A certain sense of zestfulness and adventure is also required if we are to face the ageism present in others and ourselves. Those who study the process of growing old have puzzled over this unique feature of ageism: that it is a prejudice against one's future self. It is fuelled by our inability to look at the map, ask others and embark upon the adventure of older age.

In all of this William Cutting proves himself a trusted companion on the journey. This book is the second in a four part series addressing a range of topics – here the challenges, joy and faith for Seniors. It builds upon the inspiration of book one that shows us how older people can inspire and offer us wisdom. It is honest about the difficulties and the vulnerabilities of getting older but has a tremendous sense of adventure, engagement and transformation. I commend it most warmly as a trusted map from a wise man. I wish you a happy journey through its pages!

The Reverend Canon Dr James Woodward
Canon of St Georges Windsor, author[2] and teacher
6 The Cloisters, Windsor Castle, Berkshire, SL4 1NJ
www.jameswoodward.info

---

[2] "Valuing Age: Pastoral Ministry with Older People" SPCK 2008

Introduction

Marking Time or Counting Years

Do you realize that the only time in our lives when we like to get old is when we're children? If you're less than ten years old, you're so excited about ageing that you think in fractions.

"How old are you?"

"I'm four and a half."

You're never thirty-six and a half... You're four and a half going on five!

In India people are always ahead by a year. If you have completed eight years you are "nine years running". That's the key. You get into your teens, now they can't hold you back. You jump to the next number. Young teens like to dress and decorate themselves several years older than they are.

"How old are you?"

"I'm gonna be sixteen."

You could be fourteen, but you're "gonna be sixteen".

"I'll be getting my provisional driving licence now."

Then you reach eighteen. You qualify to vote, to serve in the Army and die for your country. You swagger up to the checkout with your ID at the ready – you know, those signs that say, "If you are lucky enough to look under eighteen, you will need to bring your identification when purchasing alcohol"!

And then the greatest day of your life happens: you become twenty-one. Even the words sound like a poetic ceremony: you *become* twenty-one.

But then you turn thirty... ooohhh! The Big Three Oh – what happened there? Makes you sound like bad milk... He *turned,* we had to throw him out. There's no fun now. What's wrong? What changed? You *become* twenty-one, you *turn* thirty, then you're *pushing* forty... Stay over there, it's all slipping away...

So you *become* twenty-one, you *turn* thirty, you're *pushing* forty, you *reach* fifty – and your dreams are gone. You *make it* to sixty. You didn't think you'd make it...! Then you build up so much speed you *hit* seventy! After that, it's a day by day thing. After that, you hit Wednesday... You get into your eighties, you hit lunch. You won't even buy green bananas or the large jar of jam. "That's an investment, you know, and it may be a bad one."

And it doesn't end there... Into the nineties you start going backwards...

"I'm *just* ninety-two..."

Then a strange thing happens. If you make it over a hundred, you're a celebrity. In Britain you get a personal greeting from the Queen; you become a kid again, have a party and you can boast, "I'm a hundred and a half."

At a hundred and one, you will only get one candle on your cake…

PS. Oh! Now that I'm an octogenarian I like to keep telling myself, "Don't you know that eighty is the new sixty! Now that we have drugs like statins and Viagra, and the NHS is kindly equipping our hearts with electronic pacemakers!"

Seniors

are Vulnerable

Face the Future

Vulnerability Valued

John Wyatt, Emeritus Professor of Neonatology at University College, London, saw his role as the defender of the interests of the most vulnerable in society, tiny newborn babies. Because of their vulnerability and dependence, these tiny humans deserve the greatest effort and protection.

He believes that the Christian doctrine of incarnation, God coming to earth as Jesus did, a small vulnerable baby, has a special resonance with someone working in neonatology.[3] God in Jesus came as a tiny baby, completely dependent on the intimate care and protection of his mother. She had to do everything for him, put him to her breast for milk to nourish him and wipe his bottom to clean him. Greek philosophers and those of some other religions today find this concept of God entering the world in such a helpless, dependent state is frankly scandalous and even laughable. But was God trying to demonstrate something? Is he trying to tell us that the vulnerable and dependent have a special value?

A major vulnerable group in our society are the elderly. Some of them live by themselves – isolated, lonely and forgotten. Others are dependent elderly, who because of physical frailty or failing mentality are kept in residential homes. They need and deserve much personal care and attention. There will be increasing numbers in the coming

---

[3] John Wyatt, 'No easy answers' in 'Real Scientists, Real Faith' p.198-210. Monarch Books, 2009.

years with an ageing population. Many Seniors are carers themselves. In their homes they look after parents, partners, spouses and even dependent children.

This is a message for the frail Seniors and their carers; God values not only the vulnerable but also those who care for them. Remember this story that Jesus told:

> Then the ones who pleased the Lord will ask him, "When did we give you something to eat or drink? When did we welcome you as a stranger or give you clothes to wear or visit you while you were sick or in jail?" The King will answer, "Whenever you did it for any of my people, no matter how unimportant they seemed, you did it for me."
>
> *Matthew 25:37-40 (CEV)*

Giving personal care to the vulnerable is a work for Jesus. The mundane and the messy, the demanding and the dirty, the repetitive and the repugnant jobs for the needy are something that God values, commends and is concerned about.

There is no retirement age from this job that Jesus gives us all.

Prayer

Lord God, the stamp of your image is on every person, from
the tiny premature baby to the frail elderly who have
forgotten who they are.

Give us the compassion to care for those unable to care for
themselves.

Help us to do it with skill, gentleness, patience and always
with love.

Amen.

The Value of Old Age

A letter from one old friend to another[4]

Dear Amelia,

Time is passing and I thought that I should send you a word of encouragement. Remember, old folks are worth a fortune, with silver in their hair, gold in their teeth, stones in their kidneys and gas in their bowels.

I have become a little older since I saw you last and things have changed in my life, but I think of myself as an Antique, older, more valuable and more sought after!

I'm also quite a frivolous old girl now! I am seeing five or six gentlemen each day.

As soon as I wake up, Will Power helps me get out of bed, then I go to see John. Actually sometimes I have the urge to see him during the night.

At breakfast, Mr Quaker helps me with my oats. They leave and Arthur Ritis shows up and stays the rest of the day. He doesn't stay in one place very long, so he takes me from joint to joint. After such a busy day I am ready for bed with Johnny Walker. What a life – and, oh yes, I am flirting with Al

---

[4] From *www.tellmeastory.freeuk.com/religiousfunnies/6048.htm*

Zymer; he comes more frequently now and I think he may move in!

Then the Vicar came the other day and said that at my age I should be thinking about the hereafter.

"Oh I do, I do. No matter where I am, if I am in the kitchen or upstairs or in the basement, I ask myself, 'Now what am I here after?'"

Your loving friend,

Agatha.

Anon

When the Strong Become Weak

God's perspective

In his time, Eric Liddell was one of the most famous athletes in the world. In the 1924 Olympic Games he won the 400 metres race, one of the toughest distances, and did it in world record time. Most people know this part of his story, and how he pulled out of the 100 metres competition, his favoured distance, because it would have meant running on a Sunday.[5]

Few people know about the final lap of Eric's life after serving as a missionary in China. He died in a Japanese internment camp in 1945. The camp made many people sour and selfish. Langdon Gilkey, an academic at the Anglo-American University Peking, who was also interned, wrote an honest and unflattering account of life and behaviour in the camp. Eric was known for his gentle and helpful manner to everyone on every possible occasion. There were many teenagers there for whom the confined life was hard. Gilkey describes how Eric organised a range of games and activities, "pouring all of himself into the effort to capture the minds and imaginations of those penned up youths"[6]. Most of Gilkey's observations about personalities in the camp were bitter and barbed, but about Eric he wrote, "It is rare indeed

---

[5] This part of his life was commemorated in the film 'Chariots of Fire'.
[6] 'This is the man who runs with God'; Idle, Christopher.

that a person has the good fortune to meet a saint, but he came as close to it as anyone I have ever known."

In the second year in the camp Eric's once powerful body was reduced to frail wreck by a brain tumour. In his very weakness he made a powerful impact. Fellow prisoners who were cynics saw Christ in his life. They paid him more sincere and telling compliments than the adulation received from his Olympic success. The last words from this powerful man who had been an international in rugby football and athletics were a commitment to his Lord Jesus; he said, "It's complete surrender."

God's ways are sometimes the opposite of the world's standards. In the Greek town of Corinth the Christians were not spectacular and had many weaknesses, but they had made an impact. Paul wrote to them, pointing this out but saying that God used them because of their weakness so that He could receive the praise![7]

---

[7] References:
(1) 'The Flying Scotsman. A biography.'; Magnusson, Sally; published by Quartet Books Inc. Namara Group, 360 Park Avenue South, Suite 1300, New York, 10010, NY, USA (1981); ISBN 0-7043-3379-0
(2) 'Shantung Compound – The story of men and women under pressure.'; Gilkey, Langdon B.(1919-2004); published by HarperCollins Publishers, 10 East 53rd Street, New York, 10022, NY, USA. (1966) ISBN 0-06-063112-0

My dear friends, remember what you were when God chose you. The people of this world didn't think that many of you were wise. Only a few of you were in places of power, and not many of you came from important families. But God chose the foolish things of this world to put the wise to shame. He chose the weak things of this world to put the powerful to shame. What the world thinks is worthless, useless, and nothing at all is what God has used to destroy what the world considers important. God did all this to keep anyone from bragging to him. You are God's children. He sent Christ Jesus to save us and to make us wise, acceptable, and holy. So if you want to brag, do what the Scriptures say and brag about the Lord.

1 Corinthians 1:26-31 (CEV)

As we get older, our bodies become weaker, but sometimes our witness in that very state can be more powerful. In our weakness our witness can be powerful, because it is not what we do but what God in Jesus has done for us and can do through us that really matters. The spirit can shine out.

Eric Liddell was at Eltham College, the school and the home for the sons of missionaries, 1908-1920. Another later Elthamian, Christopher Idle, has written two hymns relating to Eric's life and to the Olympic Games. One of them, which he has kindly given permission to share, is shown opposite. It contains references to Eric's life and also allusions to athletics from the letters of St. Paul, who compares some aspects of the Christian life to a race.

This is the man who runs with God!

This is the man who runs with God!
Who aims where such forerunners trod?
He sets the pace, he wins the crown;
he spends his life, he lays it down.

This is the place where he is known;
in China born, at Eltham grown,
the Scotland star who will not fade,
who loves the day the Lord has made.

This is the day, the first and best,
of praise and prayer and Sabbath rest;
for Christ is risen, Christ is ours
for heart and mind and all our powers.

These are the feet that bring good news;
when Christ commands, who dares refuse?
For us he came, for us he died;
be strong; the Lord is on our side!

This is the cost, the body's breath
to love, to laugh, through war and death;
by blood and tears the track is hard,
but untold joy is Christ's reward.

This is the goal, the end of pain;
to live is Christ, to die is gain!
Praise God for all whose race is won
and each new life in Christ begun.

Words by Christopher Idle, January 2002

Prayer

Lord God, your standards and your ways are sometimes shockingly different from those of the world. Who could imagine that...

- a baby born in a cow shed, his family forced to flee as refugees, could be the Saviour of the world?
- a man, whose only property at the end was the clothes he wore, could endow the gift of Grace, a treasure beyond price?
- a lonely prisoner tortured, flogged and killed by crucifixion could, by that very degrading death, draw countless millions of people to his message of hope and love?

Lord, in our weakness, frailty and dependence use us and our witness for the Lord Jesus.

Amen.

Most Seniors are Far From Senile

No one believes Seniors...

An elderly couple were celebrating their fiftieth wedding anniversary. They had married as youthful sweethearts after being at school together. After they retired they had moved back to their old neighbourhood. Holding hands, they walked back to their old school. It was open, getting ready for the new term next week. They found their favourite classroom where they had sat at the back. The old wooden desk with their carved names – "Andy loves Sally" – had been replaced with some modern rubbish.

On their way back, they were nearly home, when a security van turned the corner sharply and, unbelievably, a package fell out, practically landing at their feet. The van did not stop, so Sally picked it up and they took it home. There, she opened it and in astonishment found it contained money. She counted it out: fifty thousand pounds!

Andy said, "We've got to give it back."

Sally said, "It's a love gift from Providence for old times' sake." She put the money back in the bag and hid it under their stairs.

The next day, two police officers were enquiring around the neighbourhood, looking for the lost package, and knocked on their door. "Pardon me, did either of you find a bag that fell out of a security van yesterday?"

Sally said, "No."

Andy said, "She's lying. She hid it under the stairs."

Sally said, "Don't believe him; he's getting senile."

The officers turned to Andy and began to question him. One said, "Tell us the story from the beginning."

Andy said, "Well, Sally and I used to go to the school up the road, and when we were walking home from school yesterday..."

The first police officer turned to his partner and said, "I think we'd better go!"

Many people think Seniors are senile.
Some are struggling with the truth,
and others are lying about their state of affairs,
most are experienced travellers
    coping OK on their journey of life.

A Senior Moving Home – Always a Challenge

Millicent is over ninety years old. A widow for many years, she lived in a flatlet adjacent to her daughter and son-in-law. It was a mutually convenient situation, and her little church with a group of friendly and supportive Senior ladies was just around the corner. Suddenly she heard that her son-in-law had lost his job and that he and Milli's daughter were going to move to the South of Spain. Perhaps from there they could continue their business through the internet and ease into retirement on the Costa del Sol. It sounded the ideal solution for them – but for Millicent, who would have to go too, it was alarming. When you are young, moving home can be exciting, but for many Seniors it is scary. For Millicent it was very distressing.[8]

God said to Abram, "Move!"

The LORD had said to Abram, "Go from your country, your people and your father's household to the land I will show you. I will make you into a great nation, and I will bless you; I will make your name great, and you will be a blessing. I will bless those who bless you, and whoever curses you I will curse; and all peoples on earth will be blessed through you." So Abram went, as the LORD had told him; and Lot went with him.

---

[8] Based on a true situation in 2010

Abram was seventy-five years old when he set out from Harran. He took his wife Sarai, his nephew Lot, all the possessions they had accumulated and the people they had acquired in Haran, and they set out for the land of Canaan, and they arrived there. Abram travelled through the land as far as the site of the great tree of Moreh at Shechem. At that time the Canaanites were in the land. The LORD appeared to Abram and said, "To your offspring I will give this land." So he built an altar there to the LORD, who had appeared to him. From there he went on toward the hills east of Bethel and pitched his tent, with Bethel on the west and Ai on the east. There he built an altar to the LORD and called on the name of the LORD.

Genesis 12:1-8 (NIV)

In this key story of the Old Testament we have a Senior, Abram, seventy five years old, starting out on a journey into the unknown. When you are young, you are eager to see something of the world so leaving home is natural and a journey is an adventure. When you are older, and you have a settled household with family, possessions and local contacts (the situation of Abram), moving is a big effort and a serious undertaking. Frankly it is easier to stay put with the familiar, but Abram obeyed God, with remarkable long term consequences!

When you are older, you only move for a reason. Sometimes you have to move because you have retired and the house went with the job. You may now have the opportunity to move to your dream location or to be nearer to members of your family. Perhaps the household is smaller and you want to downsize to a place that's easier to look after. Sometimes you cannot cope on your own and have to move. Perhaps you move to a retirement village, an apartment, or to a nursing home, "the final resort".

The most important reason for moving is to be in the place that God wants you to be. Few of us have such clear and specific instructions as Abram, but before moving, all of us should ask, "Am I moving to where God wants me to be?" If the answer is yes, then we know that wherever it is, we can be at home there. Sometimes, as for Milli, it is not what we would have chosen; but wherever we go, our safekeeping lies not in the place where we live but in God himself. With God we know that we will reach the heart's true home, heaven.

Prayer

Father God, please guide me in every move I make. Please be both my travelling companion and my destination.

Thank you for the words of Jesus that "My Father's house has plenty of room; if that were not so, would I have told you that I am going there to prepare a place for you?" (John 14:2, NIV)

Amen.

Help for Seniors who have to move

See two recent booklets from the charity ageUK:

- 'Housing options – Different types of housing to suit your needs'
- 'Care homes – Finding the right care home'

Also, see the following article from 'Which?' magazine, August 2010, p56-59.

- 'Get a fairer deal on SHELTERED HOUSING'

Unexpected Help

Seniors learn to accept unexpected help.

An old man lived alone in a village. He wanted to dig over his garden to plant the potatoes, but the ground was hard, his back ached, his spade seemed heavier and his arms weaker than when he was young. His only son, who would have helped him, was in prison. The old man wrote a letter to his son:

Dear Mike,

I am feeling bad because it looks like I won't be able to plant my potatoes this year. I hate to miss doing this because your mother always loved the home-grown vegetables. I'm just getting too old for the digging. If you weren't in prison I'm sure you would dig the plot for me.

Love,

Dad.

The son sent a postcard in reply:

For Heaven's sake, Dad, don't dig up the garden! That's where I buried the guns!

Your loving son,

Mike.

Early the next morning, four men arrived at the old man's house. They were from the local police force and the CID (Criminal Investigation Department). They dug up the whole garden without finding any guns.

Confused, the old man wrote another note to his son telling him what happened. The next card from his son read:

Dear Dad,

Sorry I could not come to help with the digging myself, but I sent some friends to do the heavy work. Go ahead and plant your potatoes. Hope I will be home in time for the harvest.

Love from Mike.

Remember the story about General Naaman, commander of the King of Syria's mighty army (see 2 Kings 5:1-14)? To his horror he discovered that he had leprosy. A slave girl in Naaman's household told his wife of an Israelite prophet, Elisha, who had a reputation for curing such conditions. So Naaman was persuaded to ask for his help. The treatment prescribed was to wash seven times in the little river Jordan.

"Ridiculous!" shouted Naaman. "We have bigger and cleaner rivers in our own country."

However, his servants persuaded him to give it a try, and to his amazement the condition was completely cured.

God sometimes answers our prayers in unexpected ways. Sometimes he says, "Yes!" On other occasions he says, "Wait!" Sometimes he says, "No!" And sometimes he has a completely different way of responding. We have to keep praying with faith, following God's instructions, and keep our eyes open to see what unexpected things God has for us and what unexpected people he sends to help us.

Prayer

Lord God, my loving Father, you know the things that I think I need in life, the things I keep asking you for.

Forgive me if in selfish blindness I ask for the wrong things. Forgive me when I get impatient for your response. Forgive me that I often have such a short-term perspective of life.

Open my eyes to know I need patience rather than a quick fix response. Open my eyes so I can see that you may have a different way to respond. Open my eyes to see my little life in the context of eternity.

Lord God, the life, the death and the resurrection of Jesus was such an unexpected answer to the sorry situation of the world, but thank you for your unique plan.

Amen.

Seniors can Model Contentment

What do you need to be content? In America, a while ago, a survey was conducted to find out what was a sufficient income to ensure contentment. Those receiving $25,000 to $30,000 per year said that if they earned $60,000 they would be content. Those earning $50,000 to $75,000 per year felt that if they earned $150,000 per year they would be content. Across a wide range of incomes people believed that if they earned about double of what they now received, they would be content.

Is it ever possible to be content? And of course money, though important, is only one facet of life.

A ninety-two-year-old, well-poised man was known to be fully dressed each morning by eight o'clock, freshly shaven and hair combed, even though he is registered as blind. He was moving today to a nursing home. He had carried many responsibilities and negotiated the ups and downs of a busy life, but his wife of sixty years had recently died, making the move necessary. After a long and patient wait in the lobby of the nursing home, he smiled when told his room was ready.

As he manoeuvred his walker, his zimmer, into the lift, the Home Warden gave him a cheerful description of his tiny room, its furnishings and even the floral curtains at his window.

"I love it," he stated with the enthusiasm of an eight-year-old having just been given a puppy for his birthday.

"But, Mr. Jones, we haven't reached the room yet; just wait."

"Thank you, but my contentment comes from something deeper. From experience, I have learned that I can rely on the faithfulness and promises of God. So I can arrange my mind ahead of time. It does not depend on the space or how the furniture is arranged. I have already decided to love it. When I wake each morning, it is a decision I make based on trust. I have a choice: I can spend the day in bed dwelling on the difficulty I have with the parts of my body that no longer work, or I can get out of bed and thank God for the parts that do. Each day is a gift, and even if my eyes don't work, I can focus my mind on all the good things that I have seen and shared in."

Focus is important. Near the end of his full life, when he was in prison, chained to a guard and under sentence of death, Paul of Tarsus wrote this to his friends in the town of Philippi in Greece:

> ...for I have learned to be content whatever the circumstances. I know what it is to be in need, and I know what it is to have plenty. I have learned the secret of being content in any and every situation, whether well fed or hungry, whether living in plenty or in want. I can do all this through him [Jesus Christ] who gives me strength.
>
> *Philippians. 4:11-13 (NIV)*

Ponder...

First, Paul "learnt" to be content. It was not an inborn component of his nature, but he learnt from his experience of life and his trust in God. Contentment is not getting what you want, but it is learning to focus, appreciate and enjoy what God has given you.

Second, don't compare yourself to others. There will always be other people who appear to be in a better situation than you. Usually you do not know of their difficulties and struggles.

Third, the last verse does not mean that Paul could do whatever he wanted to do. He couldn't walk on water or escape from his predicament. The Contemporary English Version's rendering of the last verse is as follows: "Christ gives me the strength to face anything." (CEV) That was the secret of contentment.

Prayer

Lord God, please forgive me that I often think that contentment depends on money and on things.

Lord, I thank you for all those who, like Paul, have learnt to find their contentment in trusting in you, in following the teaching and enjoying the companionship of Jesus. Lord God, help me to learn contentment like that.

Lord, I thank you for all the reasons I have to be content. I thank you for the physical and social provisions that I can still enjoy in my life, and I thank you that through being your child I can also rest content in spiritual security.

Amen.

ADHD, Senior Variant

Attention Deficit Hyperactivity Disorder in Seniors

The condition, ADHD, presents in different ways in different cultural, environmental and domestic situations. This is how one Senior in England described it:

I decide to wash my car.

As I start towards the garage, I notice that some letters have arrived, and I decide to read the post before I wash the car. I put the car keys down on the table, the junk mail in the waste basket under the table, and notice that the basket is full. So I decide to put the bills back on the table and take the paper to the recycling bin first. But then I think, since I am going to be near the pillar box when I take out the recycling paper, I may as well pay the bills first.

I take my cheque book off the table, and see that there is only one cheque left but three bills to be paid. My new cheque book is in my desk in the study, so I go to my desk, where I find the glass of orange juice I had been drinking. I'm going to take out the cheque book, but must first move the glass of juice so that I don't accidentally knock it over. The juice should be kept cold so I decide to put it in the refrigerator.

As I head towards the kitchen with the glass, a vase of flowers on the window sill catches my eye – it needs to be topped up with water so I set the glass of orange down on the sill, and I discover my reading glasses that I've been searching for all morning. I decide I had better put them on my desk, but first I'm going to water the flowers. I set the glasses down on the sill, fill a jug with water and suddenly I spot the TV remote control. Someone left it on the kitchen table. I realise that tonight, when we go to watch TV, we will be looking for the remote, but nobody will remember that it's on the kitchen table, so I decide to put it back in the lounge where it belongs, but first I'll water the flowers. I start to pour the water in the vase, but some spills on the floor. So I set the remote back down on the table, get an old towel and wipe up the spilt water. Then I head down the hall trying to remember what I was planning to do.

At the end of the day... the car isn't washed, the bills aren't paid, there is half a glass of warm orange juice sitting on the window sill, the flowers aren't watered, there is only one cheque in my cheque book, I can't find the remote control for the TV or my glasses, and I don't remember what I did with my car keys. Then I try to figure out why nothing got done today. I'm really baffled because I know I was busy all day long, and I'm really tired. I realise this is a serious Senior problem, and I'll try to get some help for it – but first I'll check my emails.

That takes the rest of the day!

Segments of a Senior's day
Where the time goes

Simple action points for Seniors

Do not be offended by the simplicity of these tips!

- Concentrate on one job at a time and try to finish it – even if the telephone rings or your wife says it is time to drink coffee.
- Keep a calendar prominent in your living area. It must have plenty of space to write, and note every engagement, large and small. Look at it daily while eating breakfast!
- It is often helpful to write a simple 'to do' list for your day and your shopping expedition. Lists are simple and sensible, not just for CEOs. Don't despise them.
- Have specific places to keep your keys, glasses, pen, dog lead etc. Seniors are often obsessional, but this is a useful obsession as short-term memory starts to slip.
- Sometimes it is worth having a spare pair of glasses, hearing aid, pen, front door key (kept with a good neighbour) etc.

Seniors, Hold On to the Vision

A senior doctor was determined to provide an excellent service for patients through his department in a teaching hospital. His laudable aims were to give quality patient care and also sound training for young doctors in his specialty. He also wanted his unit to achieve special recognition by undertaking clinical research that would advance treatment and bring an academic accolade. In a research trial the new treatment he introduced did not provide the good results he had hoped for and so he falsified some of the data to make it appear that the new treatment was really effective. It looked dramatic, but the benefits he had reported could not be repeated by others using the same treatment. When his research was investigated, the false results were exposed. He was suspended from his post and the General Medical Council removed his name from the Register.

This is a true story of a senior doctor who had started with high ideals and hopes but in the end was frustrated, fraudulent, disappointed and dismissed in shame.

The death of Moses

Moses was one of the greatest and oldest of the patriarchs, a God-chosen leader. However, at one stage his people had gone back from worshipping God to worshipping an image, a golden calf. They, and he, lost the blessing of God (Deuteronomy 3:26-27). Moses was allowed to view the

51

'promised land' from a mountain top, but because of unfaithfulness, he would never enter it.

> Then Moses climbed Mount Nebo from the plains of Moab to the top of Pisgah, across from Jericho – from Gilead to Dan, all of Naphtali, the territory of Ephraim and Manasseh, all the land of Judah as far as the Mediterranean Sea, the Negev and the whole region from the Valley of Jericho, the City of Palms, as far as Zoar. Then the LORD said to him, "This is the land I promised on oath to Abraham, Isaac and Jacob when I said, 'I will give it to your descendants.' I have let you see it with your eyes, but you will not cross over into it."
>
> *Deuteronomy 34:1-8 (NIV)*

All this lost, Lord, just because we carved the odd image in our spare time.

There is a paradox in the last part of the story about Moses. It describes his longevity, his physical fitness and then his sudden death. Did he die from the exertion of climbing the mountain at the age of 120, or was it the disgrace of his people worshiping an image, or the disappointment of his not being allowed to attain his lifelong aim and objective?

Even in Senior years, good men and women are vulnerable to corruption. They can let their vision and standards become dim or distorted. Disappointment, frustration, professional pressure, or even greed can tempt them, and us, to cut corners and be dishonest. Even as Seniors we may strive for good objectives, but if we use wrong methods and lose our integrity, even in our later years we may fall at the last hurdle!

Prayer

Dear Lord God, thank you for the vision and example of Jesus for every stage of our lives. Forgive us for we often lose sight of this high calling.

Forgive us when we look down on others who have failed to live by your calling.

Please strengthen us to think, speak and live with integrity. Amen.

Integrity and a 'True Man' in Politics

Harry S. Truman, 33rd U.S. President, 1945-1953

Harry Truman was a different kind of President. He probably made more important decisions regarding U.S. history than any of the other forty-two Presidents preceding him. These included the end of World War II with the atomic bombing, the start of the cold war and the United Nations. There were threats from abroad, post-war economic stresses at home and corruption in politics. But, right into his Senior years he was as straight as his name!

On May 6th, 1971, when Congress was preparing to award him the Medal of Honor on his 87th birthday, Harry Truman refused it, writing, "I don't consider that I have done anything which should be the reason for any award, Congressional or otherwise."[9]

A measure of his greatness can be seen by what he did after he left the White House. When President Eisenhower succeeded him, Harry and his wife Bess simply drove home by themselves. There was no Secret Service escort.

The only asset he had when he died was the house he lived in, in Independence, Missouri. His wife had inherited that house from her mother and father, and apart from their years in the White House, they lived their entire lives there.

---

[9] Said to have been reported in The New York Times on 7th May, 1971.

As President, he had paid for all his own travel expenses and food.

When he retired from office in 1952 his income was a U.S. Army pension of $13,508 a year. Congress, noting that he was paying for his own stamps and personally licking them, granted him an 'allowance' and, much later, a retroactive pension of $25,000 per year.

When offered corporate positions at large salaries, he declined, stating, "You don't want me. You want the office of the President, and that doesn't belong to me. It belongs to the American people and it's not for sale."

Modern politicians have found new ways of cashing in on the Presidency and other offices, resulting in untold wealth. Today, many in Congress or Parliament have found ways to become wealthy through their jobs. Political offices are now for sale.

Good old Harry Truman was correct when he observed, "My choices in life were either to be a piano player in a whore house or a politician, ultimately in the White House. And to tell the truth, there's hardly any difference! They make a lot of noise but really don't have much to do with what goes on inside."

A commentator said of Harry Truman, "Dig him up and clone him! We need politicians like that."

> Better to be poor and honest, than a rich person no one
> can trust.
>
> *Proverbs 19:1 (The Message)*

Role Reversal

Our children, with a touch of pique,
Complain we're out four nights a week,
And pressingly suggest we do more resting.
They offer us some dull advice
About the virtues of brown rice
And other foods we don't thing worth ingesting.

They're urging us to sign up for
Some nice safe undemanding tour
In lieu of a far jauntier vacation,
And watch us disapprovingly
Drink every drop of our Chablis
Untroubled by their pleas for moderation.

They warn us we are sure to slip
And give ourselves a fractured hip
Unless, when climbing stair, we grip the railing.
They tell us to slow down, relax,
Lift nothing that will strain our backs,
And take a pill for everything that's ailing.[10]

---

[10] Poem taken from 'I'm Too Young to Be Seventy'; Free Press, NY, 2005; page 58. Free Press, Simon & Schuster, New York 10020.

We don't ail all that much. In fact,
We see ourselves as quite intact,
Despite some losses physical and mental.
So though we know no harm is meant,
We've come to mightily resent
Our children's tendency to act parental.

Judith Viorst[11]

---

[11] Judith Viorst is an American, born in 1931, a psychoanalysis
researcher, journalist, and author, especially of children's books and
poems that reflect on love, marriage and the passing of years.

Being Positive through Pain

Stephen Rider Smith

Nothing grips your attention like pain. When I have a simple toothache I can think about no one or nothing else. Some courageous people can cope with pain and anxiety and still show care and concern for others. My friend Stephen Rider Smith was such a man.

Stephen was one of my best friends at school, both in India and in London. He was a good all-rounder, but majored in both sports and leadership. He was the second best sportsman from Eltham College in the 20th Century. The best-known was Eric Liddell, 400 metre Olympic Gold Medallist and Scottish rugby international. Like Eric, Stephen trained as a teacher and became a missionary. Stephen was an exceptional rugby player; he played rugby for several top clubs, was captain of Hampshire County and Cambridge University teams and played for the Barbarians and England at scrum half. He suffered a lot of pain at different stages of his life. He sustained a broken rib in the Calcutta Cup game against Scotland at Murrayfield, but played on to the end of the match. Later he had a severe knee injury which continued to give him pain for the rest of his life, but did not limit his activities. In his last nine months he had a painful cancer of his spine which spread to other bones.

In 2009, the year before he died, Stephen met a man who was selling stone carvings and other crafts made by a poor Zimbabwean artists' co-operative called ArtPeace. The homes of the artists' families had been destroyed by government agents and they had lost everything, but they were given space and peace just outside of Harare by a Jesuit community and continued their crafts. This touched Stephen's heart, and he made numerous phone calls and sent many e-mails. He arranged for a concert featuring Henry Olonga, the famous Zimbabwean cricketer. He proposed and helped to organise a sculpture exhibition at his church at Marlow just months before he died. People came from near and far to see this most professional display of hundreds of exhibits. It required much thought and hard work, and amazingly raised £20,000 which directly benefited the poor artists' community in a variety of ways. Stephen, aged seventy-four, in the last year of his life, while his body was being destroyed by a painful cancer, devoted himself to working for those poor Zimbabwean families!

The most amazing example of someone showing love and concern for others when in extreme anxiety and pain was Jesus at his crucifixion. Here is a part of the story.

> Two other men, both criminals, were also led out with him to be executed. When they came to the place called the Skull, they crucified him there, along with the criminals – one on his right, the other on his left. Jesus said, "Father, forgive them, for they do not know what they are doing."
>
> *Luke 23:32-34 (NIV)*

Some of us may be too familiar with this story to appreciate its full impact. A friend of ours who was a radical Muslim, when he first read this story in the Bible, said, "This is amazing! I have never heard of anything like this." He was very well-read in Islamic literature, the Qur'an, the Hadith and other books. Here, in response to being painfully killed was not revenge but forgiveness. When he saw this account of love shown during painful suffering it was so dramatic and different that it was an important step in coming to faith in Jesus.

Prayer

Lord God, thank you for the example of those who in anxiety and pain still show love, compassion for others and forgiveness.

Lord God, when I am called to a time of suffering, either physical or emotional, please grant me strength to endure it with courage and fortitude, please grant me compassion for others who may be suffering more than I am.

Lord God, make me ever conscious and always thankful for the incredible love of Jesus, who accepted a painful death, and through that mystery paid the price for the salvation of all who trust in Him. Thank you.

Amen.

A Senior Moment

An elderly lady did her shopping and went back to the car park for her car. When she reached it she found four young men in the act of leaving with her vehicle. She dropped her shopping bags, drew her hand gun from her purse and screamed at the top of her lungs, "Get out of my car. I have a gun, and I know how to use it!" The four men didn't wait for a second threat. They got out and ran like mad.

Out of my car, boys! I have a gun and I know how to use it.

The old lady, somewhat shaken, then proceeded to load her shopping bags into the back of the car and got into the driver's seat. She was so shaken that she could not get her key into the ignition. She tried and tried, and then she realised why. It was for the same reason she had wondered why there was a football, a Frisbee and a six-pack of beer beside the front seat. A few minutes later, she found her own car parked four or five spaces further down.

She loaded her bags into the car and drove to the local Police Station to report her mistake. The Sergeant to whom she told the story couldn't stop laughing. He pointed to the other end of the counter, where four pale men were reporting a carjacking by a mad, elderly woman described as white, less than five feet tall, with glasses, curly white hair, and carrying a large handgun.

This is apparently a true account recorded in the Police Station Log of Sarasota, Florida, U.S.A. No charges were filed against the lady.

Moral from the story? When you make a mistake, own up, and when you have a 'Senior moment', make it memorable. Give thanks if you live in a community where Seniors do not need to carry a gun when they go shopping and where the society does not bring police charges against you for your forgetfulness!

Seniors may Face a Failing Memory

Mollie Smith

Seniors are sometimes vulnerable and in need of care. For the last ten years of her life, dementia robbed Mollie Smith of her true personality. She appeared to be a wizened little old lady who needed help with everything. Those who cared for her had no idea about her dynamic life of service. At her funeral it was our privilege to share with a few of her carers something of her remarkable story.

For thirty years, 1951-1981, Mollie was not only the Nursing Superintendent of the busy Christian hospital in Jammalamadugu, an impoverished rural area of India, but she was the most dynamic person there. During her time, the hospital grew from 100 bed strength to over 250, and a School of Nursing was started. She had a first class brain and coped with many medical emergencies better than most doctors. Her care for the patients was personal and hands-on. Her love of and loyalty to the hospital staff were total. Her fury at injustice was something to behold, and her devotion to duty and capacity for work were beyond anything I have known. She was consistently in the hospital before 6:30 a.m. to take the reports from the night staff as they went off duty. She admitted to regularly working a twelve to fourteen hour day, and if there were emergencies in the night, she would be there, to give an anaesthetic, to put up an intravenous drip, to help with an obstructed labour, or to tube feed a tiny premature baby. She was quality loving

63

care in action. More than any other person she kept the hospital focused on its God-given ministry. She taught scores of nurses and was a powerful role model for the whole staff. Directly and indirectly she must have saved thousands of lives. Thankfully she also had a good sense of the ridiculous and could see the funny side of people and situations!

Ironically, beyond our understanding, this mighty carer ended up with dementia and was totally dependent. Vulnerability and dependence should not be a surprise for Christian disciples. One of the last things that Jesus said to his impulsive, action-orientated lead disciple, Peter, was to prepare him for dependence on others. This is what long-term discipleship would be like. Jesus said:

"Very truly I tell you, when you were younger you dressed yourself and went where you wanted; but when you are old you will stretch out your hands, and someone else will dress you and lead you where you do not want to go."

John 21:18 (NIV)

God has special concern for the vulnerable in society, those who have no one to speak for or protect them. They deserve special care. This is repeated by several prophets and by Jesus.

This is what the LORD Almighty said: 'Administer true justice; show mercy and compassion to one another. Do not oppress the widow or the fatherless, the foreigner or the poor. Do not plot evil against each other.'

Zechariah 7:9-10 (NIV)

Many Seniors have to learn to accept care, but other Seniors are carers themselves. Some look after parents, spouses, partners, friends and even dependent children and grandchildren. God emphasizes a concern for not only the vulnerable but also for those who care for them. Seniors may pass from one role to the other, from being carers to being the cared for. For many, this latter role is the more difficult.

In her last years, Mollie was unable to communicate, but one of her own carers paid her a special compliment. She said it was a pleasure to help Mollie and be rewarded with one of her smiles!

Mother Theresa's prayer[12]

Dear Jesus, help me to spread your fragrance everywhere I
go. Flood my soul with your spirit and life.
Penetrate and possess my whole being so utterly that all of
my life may only be a radiance of your life.
Shine through me, and be so in me that every soul I come in
contact with may feel your presence through my soul.
Let them look up and see no longer me, but only Jesus!
Amen.

Where is my Sunday paper?

"*Where* is my Sunday paper?" asked the irate customer
to the newsagent down in the High Street. "Where is my
Sunday newspaper this week?

"Madam," said the girl in the shop, ever so calmly, "we
promise to deliver your Sunday paper promptly tomorrow
morning. Today is Saturday."

There was a long pause. A new thought had penetrated
intra-cranial space.

The customer was heard to mutter, "Aaahhh... That
explains why no one was at church today."

---

[12] Mother Teresa, 1910-1997, was a Roman Catholic missionary nun
from Albania who founded the Missionaries of Charity in Calcutta
(Kolkata), and became famous for their personal care for the destitute
and dying.

Music: a Path to Hidden Memory

Sir Gerry Robinson is an entrepreneur and TV trouble-shooter whose father died of dementia. In two BBC documentaries he investigated with compassion and anger the care homes for the elderly in the UK. He highlighted some terrible, and some good, standards of care in an industry that is cynically called 'Granny Farming'. It was a moving indictment of a failing service that will be needed by an increasing number of Seniors. There are already over 700,000 people with dementia in the UK who need much personal care, and the number is growing.

His programmes highlighted some examples of good practice in homes for the elderly. One example is the role of music to improve the quality of life for Seniors. In one unforgettable sequence an enthusiastic musician had a session with a group of elderly couples sitting in a circle. One of each couple had serious dementia. They were **all singing familiar songs of yesteryear. Many of those with Alzheimer's who had not been able to speak for months were singing old songs from shows, the wartime and old hymns: "There will be bluebirds over the white cliffs of Dover" and "Pack up your troubles in your old kit bag and smile, smile, smile". Music had unlocked memories in a way that nothing else could do. Looking at the couples it was impossible to tell which of each couple was the one with dementia!**

Sometimes, as Hans Christian Anderson said, "Where words fail, music speaks."

Songs can be a repository of faith and hope. Our Lord God knows that people's memories need reminders, and He is aware of the way that songs and music can be a powerful memory jogger. This is what he said:

> ...Moses, you will soon die. But Israel is going into a land where other gods are worshipped, and Israel will reject me and start worshipping these gods. The people will break the agreement I made with them, and I will be so furious that I will abandon them and ignore their prayers. I will send disasters and suffering that will nearly wipe them out. ... Moses and Joshua, I am going to give you the words to a new song. Write them down and teach the song to the Israelites. If they learn it, they will know what I want them to do, and so they will have no excuse for not obeying me. I am bringing them

into the land that I promised their ancestors. It is a land rich with milk and honey, and the Israelites will have more than enough food to eat. ... But they will get fat and turn their backs on me and start worshiping other gods. ... When I punish the Israelites and their descendants with suffering and disasters, I will remind them that they know the words to this song, so they have no excuse for not obeying me. ... Moses wrote down the words to the song right away, and he taught it to the Israelites.

Deuteronomy 31:16-22 (NIV)

Even specialist neurologists are puzzled by the workings of the brain. Often after old folk have lost much memory and logic, they retain emotional sensitivity and some spiritual awareness, and they must not be abandoned.

The Scripture Union in the UK, conscious of this, have published three new short booklets for use when memory is failing: 'Words of Faith', 'Words of Hope' and 'Words of Peace'.[13] Each has carefully chosen, familiar Bible verses and prayers, and each has a CD with evocative music, choruses and hymns.

The responses vary and may be emotional. Sometimes there may be laughter of joy or sometimes tears. One Senior who had not spoken for months and was unable to feed herself, when asked to read a Bible passage, did it without error or hesitation. In one old folk's home, a lady who had

---

[13] Scripture Union UK. *www.scriptureunion.org.uk*. 207 Queensway, Bletchley, MK2 2EB.

been completely mute for many months, after a short service and prayer responded with a resounding, "AMEN!"

Consider for yourself or those you care for, what songs from your childhood and your earlier years carry messages of joy, peace, hope and faith for you? Revise and rehearse them in your heart. Also say and sing them out loud. See below for a few suggestions. Ask elderly friends or make your own list.

Sing, or say prayerfully...

Count your blessings,
Name them one by one,
And it will surprise you
What the Lord has done.

Jesus loves me, this I know,
For the Bible tells me so.

Give me oil in my lamp, keep me burning,
Give me oil in my lamp, I pray,
Give me oil in my lamp, keep me burning,
Keep me burning till the break of day.
Sing Hosanna,
Sing Hosanna,
Sing Hosanna,
To the King.

Away in a manger
No crib for a bed,
The little Lord Jesus
Laid down his sweet head.

I will make you fishers of men if you follow me.

What a friend we have in Jesus,
All our sin and grief to bear.
What a privilege to carry
Everything to God in prayer.

The 23rd Psalm, metrical version ("Crimmond")

The Lord's my Shepherd, I'll not want.
He makes me down to lie.
In pastures green; He leadeth me
The quiet waters by.

My soul He doth restore again;
And me to walk doth make
Within the paths of righteousness,
Even for His own Name's sake.

Yea, though I walk in death's dark vale,
Yet will I fear none ill;
For Thou art with me; and Thy rod
And staff me comfort still.

My table Thou hast furnished
In presence of my foes;
My head Thou dost with oil anoint,
And my cup overflows.

Goodness and mercy all my life
Shall surely follow me;
And in God's house forevermore
My dwelling place shall be.

Note: The subject of Dementia will be considered in more detail in 'Face the Future' book 4.

The largest charity to assist the elderly in Britain is **ageUK**. This has a new series of helpful booklets. One is 'Care homes. Finding the right care home.'[14] (2010). In it are practical suggestions, what to look for in any Care Home, whatever group run it.

Alzheimer's Society has some excellent material and help:

Address: Devon House, 58 St Katharine's Way,
         London E1W 1LB
Phone: 020 7423 3500,
Email: *enquiries@alzheimers.org.uk*
Web: *www.alzheimers.org.uk*

---

[14] For ageUK visit www.ageuk.org.uk/homeandcare

Seniors can be Stubborn

Thabo Mbeki became the second post-apartheid President of South Africa in 1999, when he was nearly sixty years old, and held the post for almost ten years. He was a Senior during his years in power. Apparently he held his country together during a period of considerable stress and economic growth, and he had a number of successes in international diplomacy. Unfortunately, in my eyes he will always be the stubborn leader who refused to stand up to the corrupt and violent Robert Mugabe in Zimbabwe. Also he blindly refused to accept that the deadly disease AIDS was caused by a virus, the HIV virus.

The AIDS epidemic was rampant in South Africa. In 2005, nineteen per cent of the adult population were infected and there were nine hundred deaths each day from the disease. Mbeki and his notorious health minister, Dr Manto Msimang, completely refused to accept the viral cause of this disease and obstructed the use of anti-retroviral treatment (ART), even when the drugs were being offered freely. Indeed, Dr Manto promoted the use of beetroot, garlic, olive oil and lemon in preference to ART. A careful study comparing HIV in the neighbouring countries of Botswana and Namibia, where some ART was used, showed that 330,000 people died unnecessarily in South Africa and 35,000 newborn infants were needlessly infected with HIV.[15]

---

[15] Estimating the Lost Benefits of Antiretroviral Drug Use in South Africa; Chigwedere, P. et al.; J Acquir Immune Defic Syndr 2008; 49:410-415

Brother Thabo, am I and my baby to die? We need strong medicines, not beetroot salad!

Political leaders, many of them Seniors, are often stubborn, inflexible and intractable. Probably they see rigidity as a sign of strength, sticking to principles. Sometimes they simply, selfishly and stubbornly want to hold on to power. When Moses was negotiating with Pharaoh, the ruler of Egypt, to let the Israelites go and return to their promised land, he came up against just such an obstinate leader. When God knew how stubborn Pharaoh could be he caused a series of plagues on the Egyptians. The first few were transient.

> But when the king [Pharaoh] saw that things were now better, he again did just as the LORD had said and stubbornly refused to listen to Moses and Aaron.
>
> *Exodus 8:15 (CEV)*

Read the whole story in Exodus chapters 5 to 12.

Political leaders are not the only ones who can become stubborn. All of us Seniors can become inflexible, set in our beliefs, our ways and rigid in our routines. Compared with younger people, we feel we have been around a long time and have the experience. We may be critical of innovation and what is new because it is different from the way we have 'always done things'. It is dangerous if we come to believe that our ways are not just good but 'the *right* way'! This is particularly unfortunate when it comes to the new ways that younger people, or those from other cultures, express their Faith or the way they worship. Seniors need to be careful not to defend tradition rather than checking Christ's commands. As Seniors we need to learn to be flexible as well as faithful. If we do have rigid views, let us hope that they do not have the deadly consequences of either Pharaoh or Thabo Mbeki.

Prayer

Our Father God, forgive us that we easily see when other people are being rigid and resistant to sensible change, but we are so blind to our own stubborn and selfish ways.

Our Father God, forgive us that we sometimes claim to be standing for principles when we are really protecting our prejudices, practices, position and pride.

Our Father God, open our eyes to see what new ways you may be leading us into and grant us courage, even in our senior years, to change and move on with you.

Amen.

Seniors, Where Have You Been?

I have been in many places, but I have never been in Cahoots. Apparently you can't go there alone. You have to be in Cahoots with someone.

I've also never been in Cognito. A lonely place, I hear no one recognizes you there.

I have, however, been in Sane. They don't have an airport. You have to be driven there. I have made several trips there, thanks to those I have worked with, and sometimes even by my family and friends.

After I had bilateral orchitis, I was told I was in Fertile. But after our first son was born, my wife, who had recently been rescued from an in Conceivable State, agreed that we were now in a much better place.

I would like to go to Conclusions, but to get there you have to jump, and I am not too much into physical activity these days.

Once I was invited to a debate in Fallible, but no dialogue was possible as the other party were convinced that God was on their side.

On another embarrassing occasion I was the invited guest speaker. I had laryngitis – no one heard my speech and the excellent jokes – and then I realised I was in Audible.

When I was younger people said my behaviour was in Appropriate, but when you're old you find it is a more spacious place where people tolerate my foibles.

I have also been in Doubt. That is a sad place to go and I try not to visit there too often.

Once I have been in Debt. There are now so many people there that it is distinctly uncomfortable, and sometimes it is difficult to get out of the place.

Some said I could escape to somewhere more in Expensive.

I've been in Flexible, but only when it was very important to stand firm.

Sometimes I'm in Capable, and I go there more often now as I'm getting older.

One of my favourite places to be is in Suspense. It really gets the adrenalin flowing and pumps up the old heart. At my age I need all of the stimuli I can get.

Nowadays, if I can, I just try to avoid being in Continent!

Oh, yes, I've been in Love. It's a really good but sometimes a risky place. Occasionally a tempting path gets you off track. But it is a big place, with such varied vistas, and it has twin top destinations in the best travel guide. They are a challenge, but very worthwhile!

So here are the twin peaks:

Love the Lord your God with all your heart and with all your soul and with all your mind and with all your strength. The second is this: Love your neighbour as yourself.

Mark 12:30-31.

Life – full circle?

Two elderly gentlemen, Tony and George, from the retirement day centre in Waterlooville, Hampshire, are sitting on a bench under a tree, when Tony turns to George and says, "Hey, George, I'm eighty-three years old now and I'm just full of aches and pains. I know you're about my age. How do you feel these days?"

Tony replies with a glint in his eye, "I feel just like an infant again."

"Really?" George sounds surprised. "Like an infant?"

"Yeah," laughs Tony, "little hair, very few teeth, and I think I just wet my pants again."

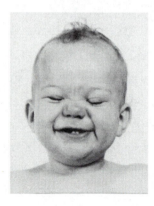

Riddle:
Why are politicians like nappies on a newborn baby?

Answer:
They should both be changed regularly... and for the same reason.

Frailty and Security after a Full Life[16]

Open your eyes, nurse, just what do you see?
    What do you think when you're looking at me?
A crabby old woman, not very wise,
    uncertain of habit, with far-away eyes,
Who dribbles her food and makes no reply –
    when you say in a loud voice, "I do wish
    you'd try."
Who seems not to notice the things that you do,
    and forever is losing a stocking or shoe.
Unresisting or not, lets you do as you will,
    with bathing and feeding, the long day to fill.
Is that what you're thinking, is that what you see?
    Then open your eyes, nurse, look deeper at me.
I'll tell who I am as I sit here so still,
    as I rise at your bidding or eat at your will.

I'm a small child of ten with a father and mother,
    brothers and sisters who love one another;
I'm a girl of sixteen with wings on her feet,
    dreaming that soon now a lover she'll meet;
A bride soon at twenty – my heart gives a leap,
    remembering vows that I promise to keep;
At twenty five, now I have young of my own,
    who need me to build a secure, happy home;

---

[16] Author of stanzas 1-3 unknown, possibly written by one of Mattie's nurses in a home in Lanarkshire. Last stanza written by William A. M. Cutting.

A woman of thirty, my young now grow fast,
    bound to each other with ties that should last;
At forty, my young ones have grown and have gone,
    but my man is beside me to see I don't mourn;
At fifty once more babies play round my knee,
    again we know children, my loved one and me.

Dark days are upon me, my husband is dead,
 I look at the future, I shudder with dread,
My young are all rearing young ones of their own,
 and I think of the years and the love that I've known.
I am an old woman and nature is cruel.
 'tis her jest to make old age look like a fool.
The body it crumbles, grace and vigour depart;
 there's now just a stone where I once had a heart;
But inside this old carcase a young girl still dwells,
 and now and again my battered heart swells.
I remember the joys, I remember the pain,
 and I'm loving and living life over again.
I think of the years, all too few, gone too fast,
 and some people tell me that nothing can last.

But one thing is certain, God's promise is sure,
 tho' my body will perish, my soul will endure.
Jesus stated quite plainly – who trust in his Name
 have a hope that is lasting, for that's why He came.
His presence is with me whatever the day,
 and His Spirit will lead me each step of the way.
Diseases all cured and sins all forgiven,
 I'll have a new body for life in God's heaven.
So open your eyes, nurse, just open and see,
 not a crabby old woman, look deeper at me.
Do not be deceived by my wrinkled old face,
 my soul's quite secure, it is saved by His grace!

Seniors can Take Up New Roles

Welcome Officer at the supermarket

Young people forget that we old people had a career before we retired...

Charley, a new retiree, Welcome Officer or greeter at Wal-Mart (like Asda in the U.K.) just couldn't seem to get to work on time. Every day he was five, ten, or even fifteen minutes late. But he was a good worker, really tidy, clean-shaven, sharp-minded, helpful to all, great and small, and a real credit to the company, demonstrating their "Older Person Friendly" policies.

One day the boss called him into the office for a talk.

"Charley, I have to tell you, I like your work ethic, you do a bang-up job when you finally get here; but your being late so often is quite bothersome."

"Yes, I know, boss, and I am working on it."

"Well, good, you are a team player. That's what I like to hear."

"Yes sir, I believe in teamwork and understand your concern, and I'll try harder."

Seeming puzzled, the manager went on to comment, "It's odd, though, your coming in late. I know you're retired from the Armed Forces. What did they say to you there if you showed up in the morning so late and so often?"

The old man looked down at the floor, then smiled.

He chuckled quietly, then said with a grin, "They usually saluted and said, 'Good morning, Admiral, do you need your coffee, sir?'"

A Senior's prayer – loss of status and position

Lord God, I remember the times when I had important responsibilities:

- I had a family to provide for, children to care for and nurture in a thousand ways.
- I had a business to run, people to teach, patients to examine, budgets to manage, timetables to plan, articles to write, deadlines to meet, reports to submit, meetings to chair, a team to inspire, people to direct, decisions to make that would affect the lives of many. Things, I felt, depended on me.

Lord God, times have changed:

- Now my decisions seem trivial and affect only myself and a few who are close.
- My children are grown. They make their own decisions and their own way.
- Those I have trained up have superseded me and moved on and up.
- I have now lost my position and feel of no importance.

Lord God, as I look back, I thank you for the things that seemed to go right:

- for children who grew and developed into useful and caring adults.
- for programmes that worked and benefited many.
- for friendships that were built and have stood the tests of stress and time.
- for opportunities and responsibilities that developed my character.

Lord God, as I look back, I ask forgiveness:

- for times when I was a poor leader or a bad role model.
- for times when I was motivated by selfishness and short term satisfaction.
- for times when I missed the opportunities that were presented.
- for times when I forgot and neglected you in the rush and pressures of life.

Lord God, at this time remind me of the eternal truths:

- that I am your child now and I always was.
- that you love me as much now as when I was busy and 'important'.
- that you died for me, paid the ransom for my wrong deeds, to buy my forgiveness.
- that I am a sinner saved by your grace, but safe in your hands.

Thank you, Lord God. Amen.

Seniors

Enjoy being Grandparents

Face the Future

Grandparents

Grandparents bestow upon their grandchildren
The strength and wisdom that time
And experience have given them.
Grandchildren bless their grandparents
With a youthful vitality and innocence
That help them stay young at heart.
Together they create a chain of love
Linking the past with the future.
The chain may lengthen,
But it will never be broken...

Author Unknown

Not everyone is privileged to be a grandparent, or to live near enough to their grandchildren to be able to frequently enjoy their company and vitality as they grow and develop. However, for some fortunate grandparents this cross-generational sharing is one of the greatest joys of being a Senior. Even if you do not have grandchildren, or if they are not close, nearly everyone can make friends with youngsters in a safe and friendly environment. Indeed, in these days of isolation and loneliness for many old people living alone, families with young children have been recommended to 'adopt a grandparent'. It can be a mutually enriching experience.

This contact across the generations is a two-way street. The stimulation and information flow in two directions. Messages of encouragement and experience from the past flow one way, and messages of hope and expectation for the future flow the other way. These contacts across the generations are as valuable as the blood that flows to the heart and lungs and then, being refreshed with oxygen, is pumped around the body again.

This section about grandparents and grandchildren is full of fun and innocent jokes to cheer our hearts. However, it starts with a big and sad story, the burden of some grandparents whose families have been struck by the HIV virus and the disease of AIDS. The elderly people in these families have had to take on full and heavy responsibilities because the middle – the parental – generation has been wiped out. Our hearts should go out to these 'full-time carer grandparents' who have been bereaved of their own children and now have to provide for their grandchildren at a stage when they themselves need love and care. They are painful recipients of the 'double whammy'!

Grandparents: Frontline Carers in the AIDS Epidemic

AIDS kills many young adults and has a devastating effect on families, especially in Africa. The World Health Organization estimates that there were 1.7 million AIDS deaths in 2011, and nearly 71% of these were in Africa. There are 15 million AIDS orphans in Africa, and because of the high incidence of the infection within marriage, many children soon lose both parents. The effects are horrific; fifty percent of children orphaned by AIDS drop out of school and, according to one survey, one in three had contemplated suicide. Stephen Lewis, former UN special envoy for HIV/AIDS in Africa, spelt out the consequences:

"You have a society where kids haven't been to school, can't fulfil even basic jobs ... and have anti-social instincts because their lives have been so hard."[17]

Traditionally in Africa, orphans are the responsibility of the extended family, and about forty per cent are raised by grandparents. Can you imagine the burden this imposes on old folk in Africa, where in most places there is little or no social service support or pension? The elderly had expected to be looked after by their children, but many find

---

[17] From a UN Article in 'AfricaRecovery', October 2001, by Michael Fleshman who quotes Mr. Stephen Lewis, UN special envoy for HIV/AIDS in Africa.

themselves looking after their grandchildren. Try to imagine this stress!

Lwabuti is eighty-one. Since her son and daughter-in-law died, she has looked after their eight children. The two oldest are now sixteen and seventeen, still live at home and support the others by working on the family land. There is not enough money to buy the uniforms and send the youngest two to school. Lwabuti knows she is not coping well, and recently the Welfare Department suggested that the two youngest should be fostered. At first she agreed, but then she had a dream that her son told her not to foster any of the children so she has changed her mind. "As long as I am here, why should any of my grandchildren leave home?" Pressures like this bear down on tens of thousands of grandparents in Africa.

Many faith-based organisations, mainly Christian, are providing a range of services for orphans and others living with the effects of HIV. One is 'Strategies for Hope' (SfH) which produces valuable manuals, books and films about ways in which communities can address the challenges of the global HIV epidemic.[18] In their booklet 'Journeys of Faith', Phumzile Zondi, a lay church leader in South Africa, reflects on the parable of the Good Samaritan.

---

[18] For 'Strategies for Hope', see *www.stratshope.org* or enquire from *sfh@stratshope.org* for details of their materials. Their 'Called to Care' toolkit consists of practical action-oriented booklets for church leaders, and 'Stepping Stones', an award-winning training package on HIV/AIDS.

In reply Jesus said: 'A man was going down from Jerusalem to Jericho, when he was attacked by robbers. They stripped him of his clothes, beat him and went away, leaving him half-dead. A priest happened to be going down the same road, and when he saw the man, he passed by on the other side. So too, a Levite, when he came to the place and saw him, passed by on the other side. But a Samaritan, as he travelled, came where the man was; and when he saw him, he took pity on him. He went to him and bandaged his wounds, pouring on oil and wine. Then he put the man on his own donkey, brought him to an inn and took care of him. The next day he took out two denarii and gave them to the innkeeper. "Look after him," he said, "and when I return, I will reimburse you for any extra expense you may have." Which of these three do you think was a neighbour to the man who fell into the hands of robbers?' The expert in the law replied, 'The one who had mercy on him.' Jesus told him, 'Go and do likewise.'

Luke 10:30-36 (NIV)

Phumzile says the traveller symbolizes a person with HIV/AIDS, and the virus has robbed the victim physically, emotionally and socially. The priest often symbolises the church or its leadership, concerned about who caused the damage, the sin, not about making life better. The Levite is like a religious person concerned with avoiding ritual defilement by touching the victim. By contrast, the Samaritan lifts the victim to safety, starts practical treatment and pays for further care. That is what Jesus implied and would have done. That is what many Christian organisations are doing as they work together. Phumzile challenges the church about its role and responsibility in the face of this epidemic. She says the church must "interpret the Bible in positive, life-affirming ways rather than to condemn people".

Prayer

Dear Father God,

Bless all family members and others who care for AIDS orphans, but especially grandparents.

Bless children who look after others in their families who have AIDS, and those who are AIDS orphans. Grant them the strength and support that they need for the grind of their daily lives.

Dear Father God, your Word repeatedly tells us to show compassion on the fatherless. Open our eyes as we read the stories and see the pictures of those with AIDS and their carers; grant us ears to hear their cries for help; stir our imaginations that we can recognise them as our neighbours; soften our hearts with Samaritan-like compassion; and show us ways that we can help those in need, both those close to us and those far away.

Jesus, may we hear your voice ring out from the Samaritan story: "Go and do the same."

Amen.

Seniors, What Does Your Life Teach Children?

Children learn what they live with[19]

A child that lives with criticism,
 learns to condemn.
A child that lives with hostility,
 learns to fight.
A child that lives with fear,
 learns to be apprehensive.
A child that lives with pity,
 learns to feel sorry for themselves.
A child that lives with ridicule,
 learns to be shy.
A child that lives with jealousy,
 learns what envy is.
A child that lives with shame,
 learns to feel guilty.
A child that lives with distrust,
 learns to be deceitful.
A child that lives with tolerance,
 learns to be patient.
A child that lives with encouragement,
 learns to be confident.

---

[19] Written in 1954 by Dorothy Louise Law Nolte, family counsellor and writer, 1924 – 2005. Modified and added to by Ronald Russell in 1971, the points with asterisks (*).

A child that lives with praise,
    learns to appreciate.
A child that lives with approval,
    learns to like themselves.
A child that lives with acceptance,
    learns to find love in the world.
A child that lives with recognition,
    learns to have a goal.
A child that lives with sharing,
    learns to be generous.
A child that lives with honesty,
    learns what truth is.
A child that lives with fairness,
    learns what justice is.
A child that lives with security,
    learns to have faith in themselves
    and those around them.
A child that lives with friendliness,
    learns that the world is a nice place
    in which to live.
A child that lives with forgiveness,
    learns to forgive others and move on.
A child that lives with serenity,
    learns to have peace of mind.
A child that lives with affection,
    learns to love. *

A child that lives with knowledge,
   learns wisdom.*
A child that lives with patience,
   learns to be tolerant.*
A child that lives with happiness,
   will find love and beauty.*

What are your children, grandchildren and great grandchildren living with? What does your life teach the youngsters in contact with you?

Seniors can Learn from Children

Truth from the lips of infants

A teacher asked a group of four to eight-year-old children, "What is love?" See their responses!

"When my grandmother got arthritis, she couldn't bend over and paint her toenails any more. So my grandfather does it for her all the time, even when his hand's got arthritis too. That's love."

Rebecca – age 8

"Love is what makes you smile, even when you are tired."

Terri – age 4

"Love is when Mummy sees Daddy smelly and sweaty and still says he is handsomer than Brad Pitt."

Chris – age 8

"Love is when your puppy licks your face even after you left him alone all day."

Mary Ann – age 5

"You really shouldn't say, 'I love you,' unless you mean it. But if you mean it, you should say it a lot. People often forget."

Jessica – age 8

"Love is like a little old woman and a little old man who are still friends even after they know each other so well for so long."

Tommy – age 6

Jesus said that adults, even Seniors, can learn from children. On more than one occasion he used the attitude of children as essential for life in God's Kingdom.

> Some people brought their children to Jesus, so that he could place his hands on them and pray for them. His disciples told the people to stop bothering him. But Jesus said, "Let the children come to me, and don't try to stop them! People who are like these children belong to God's kingdom." After Jesus had placed his hands on the children, he left.

Matthew 19:13-15 (CEV)

About this time the disciples came to Jesus and asked him who would be the greatest in the kingdom of heaven. Jesus called a child over and had the child stand near him. Then he said: I promise you this. If you don't change and become like a child, you will never get into the kingdom of heaven. But if you are as humble as this child, you are the greatest in the kingdom of heaven.

Matthew 18:1-4 (CEV)

In these passages and elsewhere, Jesus admires and recommends the humble innocence, insight and trust that we see in young children.

When a dad throws his toddler high in the air and catches him under his arms, the mother gasps, but the child laughs. That is the trust and delight that Jesus would like his children of all ages to have and to enjoy.

Prayer

Dear Father God, even as Seniors we have a lot to learn.
Please give us the insight to see the world with the innocent
clarity of young children.
Please give us the trust and love that does not question the
imperfections or motives of others.
Please give us ears to hear the loving call of Jesus as children
and adults have done for centuries.
Please give us the humility and faith to be certain that you
will catch and hold us even in the frightening situations
of life.
Amen.

Challenging words or dangerous words?

The words of Jesus about the example of children,
Matthew 18-19, awaken for me memories of Saudi Arabia.
For over ten years, from about 1980 into the 1990's, the
Department of Child Life and Health of the University of
Edinburgh ran a training programme in Riyadh. A one year
Diploma in Child Health was organised by Professor John
Forfar in conjunction with the Ministry of Health of Saudi
Arabia. Most senior paediatricians from Edinburgh used to
teach in Riyadh for a few weeks each year. It was a good
course, with a balance of lectures, case presentations and
clinical work in the Shimasi Hospital. I used to give a series
of talks about malnutrition in children and its management,
immunisations, a number of infectious diseases and the use

of epidemiology to assess child health problems. Many of the participants on that course did well, went on to obtain higher qualifications in paediatrics and became consultants. The course gave the trainers from Scotland the opportunity to see the faith of Islam in the country where it originated.

One year when I was there, probably 1992, our trainees went to the neighbouring city of Hofuf for a one day seminar in an aspect of health care and I went with them. On the return journey, we passed through a village at the hour of evening prayers, and the vehicles stopped at a Mosque so the doctors could go in to pray. I sat in the car, took out my New Testament and read the passages from Matthew, the passages about Jesus and children.

During my session with the class the next day, I mentioned that Jesus, the person they call the Prophet Essa, had some interesting things to say about children, and I told them about these passages. Since they were training in paediatrics in the culture of Islam, I challenged them to check in Qur'an and the Hadith and tell me the next day what the Prophet Mohammed had to say about children. Unfortunately I never heard their answers. The next day I was summoned to the office of the Director of the Hospital. My comments and questions had been reported, and I was forbidden to ask the trainees any questions about their faith. It was made clear that I was there to teach medical matters, and if I had questions about the Qur'an I should not ask the postgraduate students. Indeed, though my teaching had always been appreciated, year after year, I was blacklisted and was never again invited to take part in the course in Saudi Arabia.

What does that mean?

Islam has specific recommendations about nearly every aspect of life. Surely it must have some clear messages about children, their life, faith and conduct? Did the authorities not want their trainees to be diverted from paediatric studies to consider religious matters? Was I perceived as a perverting influence on the trainees?

No, I believe that the words of Jesus about the faith of children were just so challenging, powerful and different. Jesus says that true faith is not ritual but refreshingly simple, like the trust of a child. Was this so challenging that it was perceived as a threat?

What are Grandparents?

The following answers to the above question are taken from essay papers written by a class of eight-year-olds.

Grandparents are a lady and a man who have no little children of their own, but they like other people's children.

A grandfather is a man, and a grandmother is a lady, usually! Sometimes they dress funny.

Grandparents don't have to do anything except be there when we go to see them.

They are so old they shouldn't play hard or run, but they are good for driving us to the shops and giving us ice cream and pocket money.

When they take us for walks, they slow down past things like pretty leaves and caterpillars. And they don't say, "Hurry up."

They show us and talk to us about beautiful things like the colours of the flowers, and also important things like why we shouldn't step on 'cracks' between paving stones.

Usually grandmothers are fat but not too fat to tie your shoes.

Grandparents wear glasses and funny underwear.

They can take their teeth and gums out and make funny faces, but they can still eat OK.

Grandparents don't have to be smart, but they can explain about most things.

They are useful for difficult questions like "Why isn't God married?" and "How come dogs chase cats?"

When they read to us, they don't skip bits to finish quickly. They don't mind if we ask for the same story over again.

Everybody should try to have a grandmother, especially if you don't have television, because they are the only grownups who like to spend time with us.

Grandparents are good; they know we should have snacks before bedtime, and they say prayers with us and kiss us even when we've acted bad.

Grandparents are funny. Sometimes when they walk or when they bend over, you hear gas leaks, and then they blame their dog.

Communications across Generations

A grandmother was telling her little granddaughter what her own childhood was like: "We used to skate outside on a pond in winter. I had a swing made from a car tire; it hung from a tree in our front yard. We rode our pony. We picked wild raspberries in the woods."

The little girl was wide-eyed, taking this all in. At last she said, "I wish I'd got to know you sooner!"

What did you do at school, Grandma?

My granddaughter asked me, "What did you do at school?"

"Let me see. We made ginger beer in the sports cupboard, until it exploded! Then someone stole Matron's bloomers from the washing line and swapped them for the Union Jack on the flag pole. On sports day, up the flag pole went the bloomers!"

My young grandson called the other day to wish me Happy Birthday. He asked me how old I was and I told him, "Sixty-five." He was quiet for a moment, and then he asked, "Did you start at one?"

After putting her grandchildren to bed, a grandmother changed into old slacks and a droopy blouse and proceeded to wash her hair. As she heard the children getting more and more rambunctious, her patience grew thin. Finally, she threw a towel around her head and stormed into their room, putting them back to bed with stern warnings. As she left the room, she heard the three-year-old say with a trembling voice, "Who was *that*?"

My grandson was visiting one day when he asked, "Grandma, do you know how you and God are alike?"

I mentally polished my halo and I said, "No, how are we alike?"

"You're both *really old*," he replied.

A little girl was diligently pounding away on her grandfather's typewriter. (It was before the days of word processors.) She told him she was writing a story.

"What's it about?" he asked.

"I don't know," she replied. "I can't read yet."

I didn't know if my granddaughter had learned her colours yet. I would point out something and ask what colour it was. She would tell me and was always correct. It was fun for me, so I continued. At last she headed for the door, saying, "Grandma, I think that by now you should be able to work out the colours yourself!"

When my grandson Jimmie and I entered our holiday cabin, I said, "Keep the lights off until we are inside. That will stop the pesky insects from getting in, attracted by the lights."

Still, a few fireflies followed us in. Noticing them before I did, Jimmie whispered, "It's no use Grandpa. Now the mosquitoes are coming after us with flashlights."

When my grandson asked me how old I was, I teasingly replied, "I'm not sure."

Without hesitation he said, "Oh Grandma, it's easy to tell. Just look inside your underpants. Mine says, 'four to six years'."

A second grader (in class two) came home from school and said to her grandmother, "Grandma, guess what? We learned how to make babies today."

The grandmother, a little surprised, kept her cool. "That's interesting," she said, "how *do* you make babies?"

"It's simple," replied the girl. "You just change 'y' to 'i' and add 'es'."

A six-year-old was asked where his grandma lived.

"Oh," he said, "she lives at the airport, and when we want her, we just go and get her from there. Then, when we're finished having her, we just take her back to the airport."

To keep things interesting a teacher asked a little boy to "Give me a sentence including the word 'fireman' so I understand what his job is."

The boy responded, "The fireman came down the ladder pregnant."

The teacher took the lad aside to correct him. "Don't you know what pregnant means?" she asked.

"Sure," said the young boy confidently. "It means carrying a child."

A grandma was in the bathroom, putting on her makeup, under the watchful eyes of her young granddaughter, as she'd done many times before. After she had applied her lipstick and started to leave, the little one said, "But Grandma, you forgot to kiss the toilet paper goodbye!"

"My granddad is the smartest man on earth! He teaches me good things, but I don't get to see him often enough to get very smart!"

What our Grandchildren Taught Us

First, a question for Seniors: why do children who use language so imaginatively often end up as adults who use just a few short expletives?

Question: Name the four seasons.

Answer: Salt, pepper, mustard and vinegar.

Question: How can you delay milk turning sour?

Answer: Keep it in the cow.

Question: How is dew formed?

Answer: The sun shines down on the leaves of grass and makes them perspire.

Question: What is a planet?

Answer: A body of earth surrounded by sky.

Question: What guarantees may a mortgage company insist on?

Answer: If you are buying a house, they will insist you are well endowed.

Question: What is a turbine?

Answer: Something an Arab wears on his head.

Question: What is a Hindu?

Answer: It lays eggs. (hen do – got it?)

Medical Questions to a Teenage Biomedical Class

Question: Name a major disease associated with cigarettes.

Answer: Premature death.

Question: What are the main parts of the body?

Answer: The body is consisted into three parts – the brainium, the borax and the abominable cavity. The brainium contains the brain, the borax contains the heart and lungs and the abominable cavity contains the five bowels, A, E, I, O, and U.

Question: What is the fibula?

Answer: A small lie.

Question: What does 'varicose' mean?

Answer: Nearby.

Question: Give the meaning of the term 'Caesarean Section'.

Answer: The caesarean section is a district in Rome.

Question: What is a seizure?

Answer: A Roman emperor.

Question: What is a terminal illness?

Answer: When you are sick at the airport.

Question: What does the word 'benign' mean?

Answer: Benign is the age you will be the year after you be eight.

Communicating with Grandchildren

Children don't get in trouble anymore.

They merely "hit social speed bumps".

Their bedroom isn't cluttered.

It's "passage-restrictive".

They are not having a bad hair day.

They are suffering from "rebellious follicle syndrome".

No one's tall anymore.

They're "vertically enhanced".

No one's short any more.

They're "growth hormone deprived".

No one is fat any more.

They're "BMI over-endowed".

You are not shy.

You're "conversationally selective".

You don't talk a lot.

You're just "abundantly verbal".

It's not called gossip anymore.

It's "transmission of near-factual information".

The food at the school cafeteria isn't awful.

It's "digestively challenging".

Your grandchild's homework isn't missing.

It's just having an "out-of-notebook experience".

They are not sleeping in class.

They're having "a period of rationed consciousness".

They don't have smelly gym socks.

They have "odour-retentive athletic footwear".

They weren't passing notes in class.

They were "participating in the discreet news exchange".

You don't get sent to the head teacher's office.

You "go on a mandatory field trip to the administrative headquarters".

Romance and Marriage: Grandchildren's Perceptions

Seniors know a thing or two about romance and marriage. They have experienced it in many ways over many years. Still the eyes and ears of youngsters have something to share about these important subjects.

WHAT IS THE RIGHT AGE TO GET MARRIED?

"Twenty-three is the best age because by then you've known the person *for ever*!"

Camille, age 10

WHEN IS IT OKAY TO KISS SOMEONE?

"When they're rich."

Pam, age 7

"The law says you have to be eighteen, so I wouldn't want to mess with that."

Curt, age 7

"The rule goes like this: if you kiss someone, then you should marry them and have kids with them; it's the right thing to do."

Howard, age 8

WHAT DO MOST PEOPLE DO ON A DATE?

"On the first date, they just tell each other lies, and that usually gets them interested enough to go for a second date."

Martin, age 10

"Dates are for having fun, and people should use them to get to know each other. Even boys have something to say if you listen long enough."

Lynette, age 8

Say something!

She is thinking, "Will he? Won't he? Will he? Won't he?..."
He is thinking, "Shall I? Shan't I? Shall I? Shan't I?..."

WHAT WOULD YOU DO ON A FIRST DATE THAT WAS TURNING SOUR?

"I'd run home and play dead. The next day I would call all the newspapers and make sure they wrote about me in all the dead columns."

Craig, age 9

IS IT BETTER TO BE SINGLE OR MARRIED ?

"It's better for girls to be single but not for boys. Boys need someone to clean up after them."

Anita, age 9

HOW DO YOU DECIDE WHO TO MARRY?

"You got to find somebody who likes the same stuff. Like, if you like sports, she should like it that you like sports, and she should keep the chips and dip coming while you watch."

Alan, age 10

"No person really decides before they grow up who they're going to marry. God decides it all way before, and you get to find out later who you're stuck with."

Kristen, age 10

HOW CAN A STRANGER TELL IF TWO PEOPLE ARE MARRIED?

"You might have to guess, based on whether they seem to be yelling at the same children."

Trevor, age 11

HOW WOULD YOU MAKE A MARRIAGE WORK?

"Tell your wife that she looks pretty, even if she looks like a truck."

Ricky, age 10

HOW WOULD THE WORLD BE DIFFERENT IF PEOPLE DIDN'T GET MARRIED?

"There sure would be a lot of kids to explain, wouldn't there?"

Kelvin, age 8

Tea Service

Grandad in charge of convalescent

I was about three years old and had just recovered from an illness. Someone had given me a little tea set as a get-well gift and it was one of my favourite toys.

One day my mother was out and my grandad was 'looking after' me. Grandad was in the living room reading the newspaper when I brought him a little cup of 'tea', which was just water. After several 'cups of tea' and lots of praise for such good tea, my mum came home.

Grandad was pleased with his role looking after me. He made mum wait in the living room to watch me bring him a cup of tea. "It's such a cute game!"

My mother waited and, sure enough, I came down the hall with a cup of tea for Grandad. She watched him drink it, then said, as only a mother would, "Did it ever occur to you that the only place she can reach to get water is from the toilet!"

Grandma's Three Wishes

Grandma watched a DVD of Cinderella, with five-year-old Sarah.

Later that day Sarah came in with a special new painted stick which she called her "magic wand". She pretended she was a fairy godmother.

"Make three wishes," she told Grandma, "and I'll grant them."

Her gran first asked for world peace.

Sarah swung her wand and proclaimed the request fulfilled.

Next, her grandma requested a cure for all ill children.

Again, with a sweep of the wand, Sarah obliged.

Grandma glanced up at herself in the mirror, noted the wrinkles and too ample curves, and made her third wish: "I wish to look young and slim again."

The miniature fairy godmother took a look at her Grandma and started waving her wand madly. "I'll need more power for this!" she exclaimed.

Honest Granddad

A boy went out fishing in a boat with his granddad. After a few hours in the boat with hardly a bite from a fish the boy started asking his granddad some questions.

"How does this boat, that's heavier than water, float?" he asked.

Granddad thought about the question for a moment, then said, "I don't really know, sonny."

"Well, how do fish breathe underwater?"

The old man scratched his head. "I guess I don't know the answer to that one either."

"Why is the sky blue?" the boy persisted.

The granddad replied, "Sonny, I really don't know."

The boy started to worry that his granddad was getting upset at all the questions. "Granddad, do you mind me asking questions?"

The old man immediately reassured him. "No, of course not, Sonny! If you don't ask questions, you'll never learn any wisdom from your granddad!"

Probably learning honesty is a particularly valuable lesson!

Grandma Travel Service

Travel service or sales opportunity?

After booking my eighty-five-year-old grandmother on a flight, I was anxious, and called the airline to go over her special needs. The representative listened patiently as I explained and requested a wheelchair and an attendant for my grandmother because of her severe arthritis and vision impaired to the point of near blindness.

It was a relief when the airline representative assured me that I could relax; she completely understood the situation and everything would be taken care of. I thanked her profusely.

"Oh, you're welcome," she replied. I was about to hang up when she cheerfully asked, "And on arrival will your grandmother like to rent a car?"

Is this part of the 'fill in all the boxes', 'complete the checklist' mentality of those who work in call centres? She just could not visualise my grandmother!

Gifts to Grandma

Four brothers left home, became successful in their businesses and prospered. The first, Milton, became a builder and property developer; the second, Michael, became a famous singer with golden discs to his name; the third, Marvin, ran a nationwide car sales business; and the forth, Melvin, was a successful doctor.

Some years later, they met and chatted after having dinner together. They discussed the gifts they were able to give their elderly mother who lived far away.

The first, Milton, said, "I had a big house built for Mama to live in luxury."

The second, Michael, said, "I had a hundred thousand dollar theatre built in the house. So she could hear quality music any time."

The third, Marvin said, "I had my company deliver a custom built Mercedes SL600 to her."

The fourth, Melvin, said, "You know how Mama loved reading the Bible, and you know she can't read anymore because she is nearly blind? I met this preacher who told me about a parrot that can recite the entire Bible. It took twenty Bible scholars twelve years to teach him. To buy the parrot for her I had to pledge to contribute $100,000 a year for twelve years to the church, but it was worth it. Mama just has to name the chapter and verse and the parrot will recite it."

The other brothers were impressed.

She was nearly blind, so with difficulty Mama wrote out personal thank you notes in her own hand:

"Dear Milton, the house you built for me is so huge I live in only one room, but I have to clean the whole house. That keeps me busy and fit, so thanks anyway."

"Dear Michael, you gave me a fantastic theatre with all-round Dolby sound; it could entertain fifty people, but nearly all of my friends are dead, I'm hard of hearing and nearly blind. The seats are comfortable and I sit there and dream. Thank you for the gesture."

"Dear Marvin, I am too old to travel. I stay home; I have my groceries delivered. I never use the Mercedes – the road tax would be more than my pension – so I keep it round the back, pay a boy to keep it polished, but the chickens sometimes nest on the back seat. The thought was good. Thanks."

"Dearest Melvin, you were the only son to have the good sense to give thought to my real needs before sending your gift. The chicken was *delicious*! Thank you. Luv ya, Mama.

P.S. I was so surprised when I caught the bird by the neck to cut its head off, it squawked very loud some *really blasphemous words*."

How NOT to do Grandparenting

How to stop your children and grandchildren bothering you

When your children visit with their children, preferably two or three children under five years of age:

- Lecture them on how they can improve the children's
    o discipline
    o courtesy
    o patience
    o toilet training
    o bedtime routine
    o table manners
- Suggest many improvements in the ways children can be brought up.
- Emphasize to them that they should never allow their children to run riot around the house or garden.
- Explain how your children won prizes for elocution, obedience, tidiness, etc. and always start your description with phrases like
    o "In our day we..."
    o "The best way to..."

Enjoy this experience. It will be the last time you will have all the answers. It will probably be the last time you will see your children and grandchildren for a lo-o-ong time.

"In our day, children were taught to be seen and not heard!"

Grandparents' Answerphone

Hello...

You have reached the home of Mr and Mrs Jones. Please note that answers to frequently asked questions can be found on our website. Or, if you wish to speak to one of us, please choose from the following options. If you are one of our children, press 1 and then enter your six-digit date of birth followed by the hash key. Then...

- If you need us to stay with the children, press 2.
- If you want to borrow the car, press 3.
- If you want us to wash your clothes and do ironing, press 4.
- If you want the grandchildren to sleep here tonight, press 5.
- If you want us to pick up the children at school, press 6.
- If you want us to prepare a meal for Sunday and have it delivered to your home, press 7.
- If you want to come to eat here, press 8.
- If you need money, press 9.
- If you are going to invite us to dinner or take us to the theatre, start talking. We are listening and will be right back to you!

Maintain Contact with your Grandchildren

Billy Graham's book 'Nearing Home'[20], was written when he was ninety-two. It contains some practical suggestions about how he tried to share his life and faith with his grandchildren. He wanted to keep in touch, show his concern and 'bridge the gap' of years and miles. This is a summary with a few additional suggestions:

PRAY CONSISTENTLY, DAILY AND SPECIFICALLY FOR EACH PERSON

Prayer "is able to do immeasurably more than we ask or imagine" (Ephesians 3:20, NIV).

Ask that they will be guarded from temptation, will make good friends, that they will seek God's will, and that their hearts and lives will be open to Jesus Christ.

And let them know that you are praying for them.

KEEP IN TOUCH

This requires a genuine interest without appearing to interfere in their lives. Keep handy a list of their birthdays so that you can send greetings and occasional phone calls. It is worthwhile to learn how to use some social media, and texting shows you are remembering them without intruding.

They may have different dress codes and interests, but they are God's gift to you; let them know that you love them.

---

[20] Thomas Nelson (2011)

ENCOURAGE THEM

It is tempting to lecture them, but avoid majoring in negatives. Look out for what you can truly praise. In the Bible, Paul says, "Encourage one another and build each other up." (1 Thessalonians 5:11, NIV) Learn to forgive and forget if they are thoughtless or hurtful. Avoid favouritism. Remember that God made each of them and loves each of them, and so should we. Again, let them know that they are loved.

BE AN EXAMPLE

Even as you go through the disabilities and difficult times of old age, do they see in you compassion, joy and peace?

Your actions and attitudes will speak louder than words. Do they see Christ in you?

Remember that you are a grandparent and not their parent. Avoid interference or conflict in family situations. Again, the Bible has a wonderful word: "Above all, love each other deeply, because love covers over a multitude of sins." (1 Peter 4:8, NIV)

Seniors, Leave a Legacy

Have you made a will? It is the right and sensible thing to do, but one out of three people in Britain die without making a will. Your will can be a help to family and friends. If your affairs are simple, you can make a simple will and get it witnessed by two friends. There are booklets on 'do-it-yourself wills' and help can be found on the internet. If your affairs are more complicated, seek the help of a lawyer. If you have not made a will, consider the matter today.

Even more important than a will, think of the intangible legacy that your life will leave. It cannot be measured in pounds, dollars or rupees. May your legacy be a beacon of goodness, truth and loving kindness that shines a light for the next generations.

Your legacy

This is the blessing that Moses the man of God pronounced on the Israelites before his death.

Deuteronomy 33:1 (NIV)

The rest of Deuteronomy 33 is filled with the blessings that Moses leaves with the various tribes.

Jesus' legacy is truly unique, and he also left several special gifts:

> Peace I leave with you; my peace I give you. I do not give to you as the world gives. Do not let your hearts be troubled and do not be afraid.
>
> *John 14:27 (NIV)*

When my grandmother was eighty-three she gave me a special present. It was a leather-bound Bible which also contained maps, numerous pictures, a little concordance and many notes about the characters and history of the people within its pages. What made it special was that the Bible had been given to her just before she and her husband, William Cutting, sailed for India where they worked as missionaries for nearly thirty years. Inside the front cover, copper-plate writing declared:

> "Presented to Mrs Jane Eliza Cutting by members of her Bible Class as a token of the love and esteem in which she is held by every member. August 25th, 1893."

Below this, she had written, in her typical shaky hand:

> "I pass this book on to my very dear grandson – William Cutting, with very much love and all good wishes this Christmas 1951."

That was my last year at school.

My Grandmother had a tough life. Her three children were born in India, and two died before they were three years old. Her husband, William, died in 1924, and she suffered with Tropical Sprue all her life after living in India. She never had much of this world's goods, but she certainly intended to pass on to me her greatest treasure: her Bible and its priceless message of God's grace.

William and Jane Cutting (in India, 1902)
with Phyllis 1901-1904
& Cecil 1897-1984 (my dad, in sailor suit)

In fact, she passed on many other things by the way that she ordered and conducted her life. My brother and I used to stay with her during our school holidays when she was in her eighties. She welcomed a couple of lively and hungry young teenagers into her little flat. The food available just after World War 2 was meagre, and cooking facilities were primitive by modern standards, but she insisted on preparing a proper cooked lunch every day. She had an indomitable spirit and a Christian faith that was symbolised by her precious Bible. We were privileged to know her and learn from her.

Jane E. Cutting 1868-1957 (in England, 1954)

You do not have to be a millionaire to leave a legacy! We will all leave a legacy of some sort. What legacy will you or I leave? Inevitably our lives will influence those around us and especially our family members: children and grandchildren. What will the next generations take from, and remember about, you? From you they will learn about the realities of old age and how to cope with them. Will it be a legacy of love for others, generosity, integrity and inspiration, or a legacy of small-minded complaining, bitterness and selfishness?

As I hold that treasured old book in my hands I think, "I can only leave my grandmother's Bible to one of my grandchildren, but what am I leaving to all of them? How can I pass on to them the most important things in life – the eternal values of my Christian faith and the deepest joys of family and friendship?" These can only be transmitted by teaching and example, by what I say and how I live. It must be authentic, for a Christ-like character cannot be faked, and young people have a built-in detection for hypocrisy. You will need an exemplary, happy and generous life if you hope to follow the man who wrote:

> "I don't want my life to be defined by what is carved on a tombstone. I would like my legacy to be written on the hearts and lives of those with whom I have shared myself."

Prayer

Loving Lord God, I came into this world with nothing, naked, but with the gift of life. My parents, siblings, teachers, mentors and friends gave me many further gifts. Some of these gifts were physical for my health and comfort, but many gifts were intangible like love, wisdom and encouragement.

And, Lord God, the greatest gift I received was your love in the Lord Jesus.

Now, Lord, help me to give something back to enrich the lives of others.

- Make me generous with material things, for I will take nothing with me when I die.
- Make me generous with my time for it is a truly valuable gift to others.
- Make me generous of heart that I may give of myself, unconditionally.
- Make me generous with my faith; help me to share the precious friendship of Jesus.

Amen.

Making a Will, the Practicalities

"It's not that I'm afraid of dying. I just don't want to be there when it happens."

Attributed to Woody Allen

Sorry, Woody, you *will* be there. But the important thing is how you have prepared yourself legally, socially and spiritually for that time. Only you can make it easier for your family.

Benjamin Franklin said, "Only two things in life are certain: death and taxes." Both things may come together! We are all going to die, and we cannot do anything about that, but we can pre-empt and limit the financial damage and loss when it happens. 'Making a will' can limit death duties, and it is essential to ensure that your property and other assets are passed on according to your wishes and intentions. It will also limit any disputes and misunderstandings in your family. Through a will you can make a continuing contribution to a cause or charity that you think is really important.

Making a will is sensible, but only about sixty per cent of people in Britain have made a will before they die. They put it off because they don't want to think about the possibility of not being around in the future. Are you in denial?

If a married person with children dies without a will, their spouse might only inherit the first £125,000 of the estate, which may be significantly less than the value of the

135

family home. She or he could be forced to move from the home. (The precise amount of tax-free inheritance will be different in other countries and will change with the Budgets.)

If your circumstances are straightforward, you can safely write your own will using an online will-writing service or a will pack. However, mistakes can leave a will invalid. Therefore, Paul Elmhirst, author of 'The Which? Guide to Wills and Probate' (2009 edition), advises that for most people it is sensible to use a solicitor or qualified will writer.

The business of making a will can be quite straightforward, and it won't cost the earth provided you are aware of the major pitfalls.

Ten tips for a sound and sensible will

CHOOSE WISELY WHO DRAWS UP YOUR WILL

You can make your own will using a DIY kit available from the local stationers or the internet. If your life and property are complicated, it is easy to make a mistake. Lawyers make more money sorting out badly written wills and dealing with claims than from drawing up wills. So if your affairs are complicated it is better to go to a reliable lawyer.

CHOOSE YOUR EXECUTORS CAREFULLY

Executors are responsible for dealing with your estate in accordance with your instructions after you have died. It is a responsible role, and may involve handling sums of money and much paper. Ask the people you choose if they are willing to take on the role and tell them where to find the will.

APPOINT A SUBSTITUTE EXECUTOR

Some married couples choose their spouse to be executor – but don't appoint them as your sole executor! If you both died together in a plane crash or a car accident, neither of you would have an executor living. Always appoint an additional or substitute executor in case your spouse is unwilling or unable to act.

APPOINT GUARDIANS IF YOU HAVE CHILDREN UNDER EIGHTEEN

If you are the last living parent and you die leaving children under age eighteen, if you have not specified a guardian in your will, the court may do this in a way that is not best for the children.

APPOINT TRUSTWORTHY TRUSTEES

This sounds obvious, but if your beneficiaries could be aged under eighteen when you die, you will need to appoint trustees. They will be responsible for managing and investing money, or looking after property, until it passes to the beneficiaries. Make sure they understand financial matters – and are still young enough so they don't die before you do.

MAKE SPECIFIC LEGACIES

If you want to preserve family heirlooms or items of special sentimental value – for example, a grandfather clock, or a wedding or engagement ring – write that these items are a specific legacy to a named beneficiary.

MAKE SURE YOU LEAVE A RESIDUAL LEGACY

The 'residue' is what is left over in your estate after you have made any specific legacies. You must specify who this goes to. If you fail to do this, your will is incomplete, it is a partial intestacy; then the residue would be subject to the laws of intestacy and your chosen beneficiaries may lose out.

SAVE TAX WITH A TRUST

Inheritance tax in the U.K. is a burden for many families. This happens where the value of a property pushes the value of an estate above the nil rate band for inheritance tax. If you are married, you can include a discretionary trust in your wills. At present it could save your children over £100,000 in inheritance tax. This may change with each Budget. It is better to take the help of a lawyer when making such a trust.

SIGN AND DATE YOUR WILL, AND GET THE SIGNATURES OF TWO WITNESSES.

You must sign and date your will in front of two independent witnesses, or it will not be valid. The witnesses can be any adults who are not mentioned in the will or married to anyone mentioned in the will. The witnesses must also sign the will, give their addresses and the date. These signatures and dates are important.

STORE THE WILL SAFELY

Once signed and witnessed, store the will in a proper safe place. This will protect it from fire, flood, damage, or loss. Give your executors a copy of your will or tell them where the will is stored and how to get hold of it when you die. Do not hide your will. Your will is no good to anyone if it cannot be found after your death!

Remember that circumstances change. It is worth reviewing and possibly revising your will periodically. Your family and beneficiaries may have changed.

DISCLAIMER

Note that the matters specified above relate to the legal position in the United Kingdom in 2013, and may not be valid for other places and later dates.

One way to avoid Inheritance Tax

Last Will and Testament:
"Being of a sound mind, I spent all my money."

Anon.

Example of a Will

Below is an example of a simple will. You can modify and use this. Properly signed, dated and witnessed, it will be valid.

This is the last will and testament of me, [Simon Peter bar Jonah] of [Cana in Provence of Galilee]. I revoke all earlier Wills made by me. I wish that my body be [buried in the family plot in Cana]. I appoint [my wife, Rebekah,] to be my first Executor and [my brother, Andrew bar Jonah,] my substitute Executor. In this will the expression "My Trustees" means my Executors and Trustees of this Will.

I give and bequeath to [Rebekah, my wife,] all my property both real and personal whatsoever and wheresoever absolutely provided that [Rebekah] survives me by at least thirty days. I give and bequeath [my boat, 'The Spirit of Galilee', with all requisite equipment] to [John Mark,] free of inheritance tax. I give and bequeath [One Hundred and Fifty Shekels] to ['The Way of Life' Fellowship of Cana,] free of inheritance tax.

I give all the residue of my Estate (out of which shall be paid my funeral expenses and debts) to my Trustees on trust.

Attestation. In witness whereof I have set my hand this day, [March 10 in the year of our Lord forty-two.] *(insert full date)*

Signed by the said [Simon Peter bar Jonah] – *Simon Peter bar Jonah* – the Testator as and for his last will and testament in the presence of us both being present at the same time at his request and in his presence, and in the presence of each other have subscribed our name as witnesses –

Signed by the above named [Simon Peter bar Jonah] in our joint presence and then by us in his. [Nathan Israel] – *Nathan Israel* – *(Address and date written in)*

Signed by the above named [Simon Peter bar Jonah] in our joint presence and then by us in his. [David Isaiah] – *David Isaiah* – *(Address and date written in)*

Note: of course, the Apostle Peter probably did not write a will, and anyway it would not have been valid as he was killed, probably crucified, possibly upside down (which was his wish), as a criminal against the State, in Rome. He was one of many Christian martyrs of that early era of persecutions.

A Cautionary Tale

Will-writing fraud: the final payment

Bob and Marion were active seventy-year-olds, with no major health problems, so they had put off doing anything about making a will, but they had been thinking about it. Then a nice young lady, Janice Frauld, phoned from Affinity Legal Services and offered to come around and organise a straightforward will for them both for £85 plus the 20% VAT.

She was very business-like and had taken down all their details. It seemed that things were not completely straightforward, with two children, an extra stepson and uncertainty about a suitable person to act as executor. Janice said that Affinity could offer a package to not only write the wills, but also store them in fireproof vaults and provide a reliable executor. The following week she was back with all the papers typed up and ready for signature. In the end the whole package was going to be £280 with the storage etc. Bob and Isabel thought that was still reasonable and felt that it would relieve the children of any anxiety or bother. They checked that the figure on the form was all they would have to pay; Janice reassured them and they signed up.

Two years later Bob had a severe stroke and died within days. Janice Frauld had left Affinity, and the new girl took a long time to locate the wills and papers. When it came to the settlement, Marion was shocked to note that the bill from Affinity Legal Services included a charge of 1% of the total estate, and sure enough it was in the small print that Janice had not pointed out during the transactions. Further enquiries revealed that will writers do not have to be registered or insured.

If your will is at all complicated it may be wise, and economical in the long run, to employ a reliable solicitor who specialises in trusts and wills.

The Last Hoorah

When I was young and in the dawn,
I rose to put my trousers on
For some adventurous new day
Of shining sun and making hay,
There was no sense of deja vu,
No fears possessed me in the loo,
And when I shaved my stripling chin
I found it hard to check a grin.
Handsome and brave, devoid of cares,
I'd race to breakfast down the stairs.

Now I have drained that youthful cup,
It takes me ages to get up
And first among the day's adventures
Is finding where I put my dentures.
The bathroom mirror's ruthless light
Suggests I passed away last night
And at the door the postman knocks
With mail that's full of evil shocks
While by my plate a heap of pills
Bears witness to a dozen ills.
One simple pleasure does remain –
I'll go and change my will again.

Joe Pamanian

The Legacy of a Scot

Edinburgh resident Wullie McTavish is on his deathbed. He thinks that the end is near. He is being watched by the nurse, his wife, his daughter and two sons.

"So," he says to them, "Bernie, I want you to take the Braid Hills houses."

"Sybil, take the flats over in Morningside and Bruntsfield."

"Tam, I want you to take the offices in Charlotte Square."

"Sarah, my dear wife, please take all the residential buildings in the New Town."

The nurse is just blown away by all this. As Wullie slips away, she says, "Mrs. McTavish, your husband must have been such a hard-working man to have accumulated all this property in such expensive and prestigious parts of the city."

Sarah replies, "Property? ... The beggar has the biggest paper round!"

The Last Will and Testament

...of Lawyer Charles Lounsberry, 1906

It is alleged that in the pocket of an old ragged coat belonging to one of the insane patients at the Chicago poorhouse, there was found, after his death, a will. According to Barbara Boyd, in the Washington Law Reporter, the man had been a lawyer, and the will was written in a firm clear hand on a few scraps of paper. So unusual was it, that it was sent to another attorney; and so impressed was he with its contents, that he read it before the Chicago Bar Association and a resolution was passed ordering it probated. It is now on records of Cook County Illinois, USA.

I, Charles Lounsberry, being of sound and disposing mind and memory, do hereby make and publish this my Last Will and Testament, to distribute my interests in the world to the succeeding generation.

That part of my interests which is known in law and recognized in the values of this world as my property, being inconsiderable and of no account, I make no disposition in this, my Will. My right to live, being but a life estate, is not at my disposal, but, all else in the world I now proceed to devise and bequeath –

ITEM: I give to good fathers and mothers, in trust to their children, all good little words of praise and encouragement, and all quaint pet names and endearments; and I charge the said parents to use them justly, but generously, as the deeds of their children shall require.

ITEM: I leave to children inclusively, but only for the term of their childhood, all, and every, the flowers of the field, and the blossoms of the woods, with the right to play among them freely according to the custom of children, warning them at the same time against the thistles and the thorns. And I devise to the children the banks of the brooks and the golden sands beneath the waters  thereof, and the odours of the pine woods and the white clouds that float high over the giant trees. And I leave the children the long, long days to be merry in a thousand ways, and the night and the moon and the train of the Milky Way to wonder at, but subject, nevertheless, to the rights hereinafter given to lovers.

ITEM: I devise to boys jointly all the idle fields and commons where ball may be played, all pleasant waters where one may swim, all snow-clad hills where one may coast, and all streams and ponds where one may fish, or where, when grim winter comes, one may skate, to have and to hold the same for the period of their boyhood. And all meadows, with the clover-blossoms and butterflies thereof; the woods with their appurtenances; the squirrels and birds and echoes and strange noises, and all distant places, which may be visited, together with the adventures there to be found. And I give to said boys, each his own place at the fireside at night, with all pictures that may be seen in the burning wood, to enjoy without hindrance and without any encumbrance of care.

ITEM: To lovers, I devise their imaginary world, with whatever they may need, as the stars of the sky, the red roses by the wall, the bloom of the hawthorn, the sweet strains of music, and anything else they may desire to figure to each other the lastingness and beauty of their love.

ITEM: To young men jointly, I devise and bequeath all boisterous inspiring sports of rivalry, and I give to them the disdain of weakness and undaunted confidence in their own strength. Though they are rude, I leave them to the powers to make lasting companions and friendships, and to them exclusively I give all merry songs and brave choruses to sing with lusty voices.

ITEM: And to those who are no longer children, or youths, or lovers, I leave memory, and bequeath to them the volumes of the poems of Burns and

Shakespeare, and of other poets, if there be any, to the end that they may live the old days over again, freely and fully without tithe or diminution.

ITEM: To the respected loved ones with snowy crowns, I bequeath the happiness of old age, the love and gratitude of their children and grandchildren until they fall asleep.

Suggestions for Senior Living

All Seniors, grandparents and parents may appreciate this collected wisdom.

FOCUS ON ENJOYING PEOPLE AND FRIENDSHIP

Do not focus on only indulging yourself or accumulating material things.

PLAN TO USE AND DISPOSE OF WHATEVER YOU HAVE SAVED

Use savings now for the people and causes you know and love, those who need help now. If you are healthy, travel to meet family and friends; strengthen these links. If you plan to leave any legacies, try to ensure they won't lead to troubles and splits.

LIVE IN THE HERE AND NOW

Yesterday is history,
Tomorrow is mystery,
Today is a gift from God,
That's why it is called the present.

Use your gifts: cooking, sewing, painting, writing, making music, hosting, befriending or whatever! Time is precious; use it carefully and well! There is a limited supply for each of us.

COUNT YOUR BLESSINGS

Envying what others have will only give you misery.

Check and see: God has given you much! Enjoy what you are and what you have right now. You will enjoy most what you share with others.

ENJOY AND BEFRIEND YOUR GRANDCHILDREN

Enjoy your grandchildren, if blessed with any, or other youngsters if you haven't. BUT... let your children raise their own offspring their own way.

Help with child-minding where you can, but don't let them become dependent on you.

Dependent or Pendent, I don't know which is worse.

ENJOY YOUR LIFE WITH YOUR SPOUSE, FAMILY AND FRIENDS

People who truly love you, love you for yourself, not for what you have or have done.

By now you should have learnt to negotiate, compromise, share and care, but there is always scope to polish these social skills.

Make the life of others miserable and you cannot enjoy yourself.

ACCEPT PHYSICAL WEAKNESS, SICKNESS AND OTHER PAINS

They are a part of the ageing process, but enjoy whatever your body permits you to do.

For simple exercise, keep walking and moving as much as you can every day.

Let suffering strengthen your character, not destroy it.

Don't make others suffer if or when you are suffering.

FORGIVE AND ACCEPT FORGIVENESS

Forgive yourself for foolishness and failures.

Forgive others and forget old quarrels.

Generosity of heart can bring peace of mind and spirit.

RE-CLASSIFY DEATH

Recognise death as a natural milestone, and do not be afraid of it. It is not the enemy or the end; it is not the terminus, but a staging post and a new beginning.

Prepare yourself and your family, and talk of death in a natural way.

BE AT PEACE WITH YOUR CREATOR GOD BY ACCEPTING JESUS

> For God so loved the world that he gave his one and only Son, that whoever believes in him shall not perish but have eternal life.
>
> *John 3:16 (NIV)*

> I am sure that nothing can separate us from God's love – not life or death, not angels or spirits, not the present or the future, and not powers above or powers below. Nothing in all creation can separate us from God's love for us in Christ Jesus our Lord!
>
> *Romans 8:38-39 (CEV)*

These ten suggestions/recommendations are not The Ten Senior Commandments! They do not displace The Ten Commandments, but most are based on Biblical principles and are certainly worth thinking about.

Disclaimer: Unfortunately I have repeatedly failed to follow many of the suggestions!

Remember Jesus' Commandments. Jesus did not overturn The Ten Commandments, but he emphasized two old Love commandments. Then he added a third Love commandment, directed specifically to his followers. None of these are at all easy, as his followers have sadly demonstrated for two thousand years. But these three are far more important than anything written above, or elsewhere. Seniors, strive for these, and you will be wonderful grandparents and friends to the young. Moreover, other things will fall into place!

Jesus replied: "'Love the Lord your God with all your heart and with all your soul and with all your mind.' This is the first and greatest commandment. And the second is like it: 'Love your neighbour as yourself.' All the Law and the Prophets hang on these two commandments."

Matthew 22:37-40 (NIV)

[Jesus said,] "A new command I give you: Love one another. As I have loved you, so you must love one another. By this everyone will know that you are my disciples, if you love one another."

John 13:34-35 (NIV)

Seniors

and the Spiritual Dimension

Seniors and the Sphere of the Spirit

Seniors have been on the journey of life for quite some time. They have tried and tested many things. They like the solidity of a chair that you can see and feel and sit on. They enjoy a good meal with its rich aroma, flavour, texture and warm satisfaction. But most Seniors know that there are dimensions and questions that are beyond our understanding, things that are important but cannot be tested by our five senses. For example...

WHAT IS LIFE? [21]

As far as anybody seems to know, the vast majority of things in the universe do not have whatever life is. Sticks, stones, stars, space – they simply are. A few things are and somehow are alive to it. They have broken through into Something, or Something has broken through into them. Even a jellyfish, a watermelon, they're in it with us. We're all in it together, or it is in us. Life is it.

After lecturing learnedly on miracles, a great theologian was asked to give a specific example of one. "There is only one miracle," he answered. "It is life."

- Have you wept at anything that you saw, heard or experienced in the last year?

---

[21] Based on a passage from 'Wishful thinking: A Seeker's A B C.'; Frederick Buechner; published by HarperCollins Publishers, 10 East 53rd Street, New York, NY 10022 (1973).

- Has your heart beat faster at the sight of young beauty?
- Have you gasped when you saw man's inhumanity to man?
- Is there anybody you know in whose place, if one of you had to suffer great pain, you would volunteer yourself?

If your answer to all or most of these questions is no, the chances are that you're dead.

Many seniors acknowledge the inexplicable, the transcendent; they are aware of the greater and spiritual sphere that gives some sort of meaning and sense to life with its complexities and uncertainties. The spirituality of older people should include facing the proximity, reality and fear of mortality.

In his book on 'Valuing Age'[22], James Woodward sums up the spiritual and social needs of people, and of elderly people in particular, with five major strands: to feel valued and affirmed, to love and to be loved, to hope in something in this life and beyond, to have faith and trust in someone or something, and to know security and peace.

This full sense of spirituality clearly includes our relationships with others, but for Christian believers must have its centre in God, manifest in Christ and the Holy Spirit.

---

[22] James Woodward; 'Valuing Age. Pastoral Ministry with Older People.'; SPCK (2008).

Spirituality sounds nebulous, but in this section of the book are a few true glimpses of how the spiritual touched the lives of real people, many of them in Senior years. There are a few simple thoughts about, and examples of, prayers; a few poems and songs; and of course a number of jokes – since the laughter of his children can make God smile!

Billy Graham 'Nearing Home'

"Growing old has been the greatest surprise of my life," said Billy Graham.

Billy was born in 1918 on a farm in North Carolina, USA. He became the greatest evangelist of the twentieth century, and through mega-meetings, radio and TV probably had an incredible lifetime audience of over two billion. He admitted he was not the greatest preacher, but God used him powerfully. Many people came to trust and love the Lord Jesus through his enthusiastic speaking and his campaigns, which were carefully and prayerfully prepared and thoroughly followed up. Many leading Christians of today became Christians through his preaching in many countries, including Britain; both ordinary people and celebrities like Cliff Richard came to faith through his ministry.

However, when he became an old man Billy Graham declared that all his life he had been prepared for eternity, but he had not been adequately prepared for the hard days of old age with their difficulties and decrepitude.

In his final book, 'Nearing Home: Life, Faith and Finishing Well'[23], he states, "The Bible does not hide the negative side of getting older." We must all be honest about this. Billy himself has had a catalogue of medical problems. In 1992 he was diagnosed with Parkinson's disease, he has had serious intestinal bleeding, fractured hips, prostate

---

[23] Published by Thomas Nelson (2011)

cancer and recurrent attacks of bronchitis and pneumonia. He reminds us of the words of Jesus to Peter:

> Very truly I tell you, when you were younger you dressed yourself and went where you wanted; but when you are old you will stretch out your hands, and someone else will dress you and lead you where you do not want to go.
>
> *John 21:18 (NIV)*

So Billy, who in his youth had dreamed with some real expectation of being a baseball sporting star, at the age of over ninety has to have help to stand up and walk a few paces.

However, in the chapter entitled 'Running towards home', Billy reminds us that the Bible does not diminish old age but teaches us its values and virtues. It is dotted with examples of men and women who in their later years refused to use old age as an excuse to ignore what God wanted them to do: Abram, Sarai, Moses, Joshua, Zechariah, Elizabeth, Anna and Simeon.

John wrote the Book of Revelation when he was a prisoner on the island of Patmos at the age of about ninety.

Paul described himself as "an old man" when he wrote to Philemon in about AD 60. At about the same time he wrote to his friends in Philippi:

> One thing I do, forgetting those things that are behind and reaching forward to those things which are ahead...
>
> *Philippians 3:13 (NKJV)*

Although near the end of his life and in jail, Paul did not let that or other things in the past hinder him from what he believed God wanted him to do at that stage of his life!

Billy reminds us that in old age we still have the opportunity to strengthen another who is struggling or to impact others with our testimony. Use your smile to draw someone close to you and then...

> Let me tell future generations about your mighty power.
>
> *Psalm 71:18 (CEV)*

Near the end of his book, Billy Graham reminds us of the story of the old man Simeon, who did not want to die before knowing that the Saviour had come into the world. He knew the Old Testament prophecies, and he took Jesus in his arms and blessed him.

You sense Billy Graham wants to share in this blessing, and so may we!

> Lord, I am your servant, and now I can die in peace, because you have kept your promise to me. With my own eyes I have seen what you have done to save your people, and foreign nations will also see this.
>
> *Luke 2:29-31 (CEV)*

Prayer

Lord God, I thank you for Jesus. I accept him as Lord and Saviour, and ask that when my time comes, I may 'die in peace' because I have accepted Him.

Amen.

Billy Graham drives – at speed

Well on his active 'retirement', Billy Graham was returning to Charlotte after a speaking engagement. As a courtesy for his Senior status, when his plane arrived there was a limousine there to transport him to his home. As he prepared to get into the limo, he stopped and spoke to the driver.

"You know," he said, "I am eighty-seven years old, and I have never driven a limousine. Would you mind if I drove it for a while?"

The driver said, "No problem. Have at it."

Billy got into the driver's seat and they headed off down the highway. A short distance away sat a new, raw State Trooper (of the Traffic Police Service) operating his first speed trap. The long black limo went smoothly by him doing seventy miles per hour in a fifty-five miles per hour zone.

The Trooper pulled out and easily stopped the limo, and he got out of his patrol car to begin the procedure. The young trooper walked up to the driver's door, and when the glass was rolled down – *instant recognition* – he was surprised to see who was driving.

He immediately asked the Limo to wait, excused himself, and went back to his car and called his Supervisor. "I know we are supposed to enforce the law... But I also know that important people are given certain courtesies. I need to know what I should do because I have stopped a very important person."

The Supervisor asked, "Is it the Governor?"

The young trooper said, "No, he's more important than that."

The Supervisor said, "Oh, so it's the President."

The young trooper said, "No sir, he's even more important than that."

The Supervisor finally asked, "Well then, who is it?"

The young trooper said, "I think it must be Jesus, because his chauffeur is Billy Graham!"

The Preacher's Donkey

An old man bought a donkey from a preacher. The preacher told the old man that this donkey had been trained in a very unique way, being a preacher's donkey.

"He is stupid but very obedient. The only way to make the donkey go, is to say, 'Hallelujah!' The only way to make the donkey stop, is to say, 'Amen!'"

The old man was pleased with his purchase and immediately got on the animal to try out the preacher's instructions.

"Hallelujah!" shouted the man.

The donkey began to trot.

"Amen!" shouted the old man.

The donkey stopped immediately.

"This is great!" said the man. With a "Hallelujah!" he rode off very proud of his new purchase.

The next day the old man travelled a long way into the mountains. Soon he saw he was heading towards a cliff. Like many Seniors, his memory sometimes failed him. He could not remember the word to make the donkey stop.

"Stop!" said the old man. "Halt!" he cried.

The donkey just kept going.

Then he remembered it was the preacher's donkey. "Oh, no... BIBLE!... CHURCH!... PLEASE STOP!" shouted the old man.

The donkey just began to trot faster.

High in the mountain he was getting dangerously close to the cliff edge. Finally, in desperation, the Senior decided to pray.

"Please, dear Lord God, please make this donkey stop before I go off the cliff at the end of this mountain. In Jesus' name. AMEN!"

The donkey came to an abrupt stop just one step from the edge of the cliff. What a wonderful relief and answer to prayer!

Then the old man threw his hands in the air and shouted, "HALLELUJAH!"

Seniors are Never Too Old to Share Good News

Francis Collins is a leading scientist and a medical doctor in U.S.A. He came from a loving and free-thinking family who were not believers. He was a brilliant academic, graduating with a PhD in physical chemistry from Yale and an MD in medicine from the University of North Carolina. He was fascinated about the way that our bodies are controlled by the genes and DNA, and he became a leading geneticist, heading the important Human Genome Project. This project has a prospect of opening out the genetic links to many important diseases. Now he is Director of the National Institutes of Health in Washington DC. But he started his career with no faith in God.

When he was a junior doctor he was looking after a number of seriously and terminally ill patients with cancer and other incurable diseases. He was struck by the spiritual faith that gave many patients peace and serenity in situations of terrible suffering and potential fear. One of his frail elderly patients challenged him, "Dr Collins, what do you believe? Have you examined the evidence about Jesus and what he said?" It was Collins' practice in life to base his actions and beliefs on what he had examined and observed. He admitted that he had not checked out the evidence about Jesus. When he did, by reading the New Testament and the writings of C.S. Lewis, he came slowly but surely to a living Christian faith.

169

Collins wrote:

"I had to admit that the science I loved so much was powerless to answer questions such as 'What is the meaning of life?', 'Why am I here?', 'Why does mathematics work, anyway?', 'If the universe had a beginning, who created it?', 'Why are the physical constants in the universe so finely tuned to allow the possibility of complex life forms?', 'Why do humans have a moral sense?', 'What happens after we die?'"

He concluded:

"I see DNA, the information molecule of all living things, as God's language, the 'Bio-Logos'. I see the elegance and complexity of our own bodies and the rest of nature as a reflection of God's plan."[24]

No one is too old or too frail to speak out for, and point to, Jesus. Based on her personal experience, rather than her scientific knowledge, an elderly, dying lady effectively challenged a brilliant young doctor. This was a critical step in his coming to faith.

---

[24] The Language of God: A Scientist Presents Evidence for Belief; Collins, Francis S.; published by Free Press, Simon & Schuster (2006). ISBN-13-978-0-7432-8639-8

The Bible contains a great story of an old lady speaking out about Jesus. She was a devout, elderly widow called Anna. This is what happened when Joseph and Mary brought their son, Jesus, to the temple in Jerusalem for a special ceremony.

> Anna, a prophet, was also there in the Temple. She was the daughter of Phanuel from the tribe of Asher, and she was very old. Her husband died when they had been married only seven years. Then she lived as a widow to the age of eighty-four. She never left the Temple but stayed there day and night, worshiping God with fasting and prayer. She came along just as Simeon was talking with Mary and Joseph, and she began praising God. She talked about the child Jesus to everyone who had been waiting expectantly for God to rescue Jerusalem.
>
> *Luke 2:36-38 (NLT)*

Anna had been waiting all her life for something special, and it happened when she was eighty-four years old! She reminds us that sometimes you have to wait a long time for God to use you, but you should be ready and waiting. Her story also shows us that you are never too old to talk about Jesus. Seniors need to be ready for every opportunity that God gives.

Prayer

Powerful God, you are the creator of the universe and designer of life. We are amazed at the vastness of space and the microscopic complexity of every living cell. We are awe-struck, and ask that this wonder will never leave us!

Generous God, we thank you that science can help us to understand and utilise many of the mechanisms of living organisms to enhance health and bring healing. We are concerned that we use knowledge and skills in the right way and to your glory. Grant us wisdom.

Loving God, we acknowledge that man's puny intellect cannot unravel the mysteries of the 'why' questions of our lives and our world. We thank you that Jesus came to answer many of the deepest questions, to demonstrate your love and to open the way for men and women to be forgiven and to know you.

Almighty God, we thank you.

Amen.

A Humble Prayer

"Christianity, if false, is of no importance, and if true is of infinite importance. The one thing it cannot be is moderately important."

C.S. Lewis

Clive Staples Lewis (1898-1963) was an Irish-born writer and scholar. An atheist from the age of fifteen, he slowly returned to faith in his early thirties. He was a friend and colleague of J.R.R. Tolkein at Oxford, where he lived for many years. He wrote many books, but is best known for The Chronicles of Narnia. His writing had a profound influence on many people.

The Apologist's Evening Prayer[25]

From all my lame defeats and oh! much more
From all the victories that I seemed to score;
From cleverness shot forth on thy behalf
At which, while angels weep, the audience laugh;
From all my proofs of thy divinity,
Thou, who wouldst give no sign, deliver me.

---

[25] C.S. Lewis, Poems (1964). Poems by C.S. Lewis.
Copyright C.S. Lewis Pte. Ltd. 1964. Extracts printed by permission.

Thoughts are but coins. Let me not trust, instead
of thee, their thin-worn image of my head.
From all my thoughts,
even from my thoughts of thee,
O thou fair Silence, fall, and set me free.
Lord of the narrow gate and the needle's eye,
Take from me all my trumpery lest I die.

Seniors can Ask for Help

During a severe flood, John's riverside house was surrounded by swirling water. He prayed to God to rescue him, and was certain that God would help him escape. A few minutes later his neighbour Jim, who lived just down the road, called him on the phone.

"John, the river water is rising, but if you make for the higher ground now you will be safe."

He replied, "Thanks, Jim. I have prayed to God and I truly believe that he will rescue me."

The water continued to rise and so John had to retreat upstairs. Again he got on his knees and prayed to God to rescue him. A few minutes later, as he looked out of the window, his neighbour Jim came up in his rubber dingy.

"Jump in, John, and I'll get you away to safety."

"Thanks, Jim, but I have prayed to God and I am confident that he will save me."

The water rose alarmingly high. John had to climb out of the top window onto the roof. There he repeated his prayer: "Dear God, please rescue me. I know that you can do this." Minutes later a police helicopter hovered overhead and lowered a rope ladder.

"Grab the ladder and come up", shouted the policeman.

"Thank you, Officer, but I have prayed to God and I know he can rescue me."

Within the hour the house was submerged and John drowned.

On reaching Heaven, John's first question to the Almighty was, "God, I prayed to you three times with great faith to save me from the flood. Why did you not rescue me?"

The Almighty replied, "John, I asked Jim to call you and advise a run to higher ground. Then I sent him with his boat. Finally I arranged the police helicopter team to pick you up. It is really difficult to help those who are not alert to see when I am trying to help them. No need to be foolish as well as faithful!"

A Senior catches the attention of the police

George Phillips, an old man, from Meridian, Mississippi, U.S.A. was going up to bed, when his wife told him that he'd left the light on in the garden shed, which she could see from the bedroom window. George opened the back door to go and turn off the light, but saw that there were people in the shed stealing things.

He phoned the police and gave his name and address. The Officer asked, "Is someone in your house?"

He said, "No, but some people have broken into my garden shed and are stealing things from me."

Then the Officer in the Police Emergency Department said, "All patrols are busy. Stay in your house, lock all your doors and an Officer will be along when one is available."

George said, "Okay."

He hung up the phone and counted slowly to a hundred. Then he phoned the police again.

"Hello, I just called you a few minutes ago because there were people stealing things from my shed. Well, you don't have to worry about them now because I took out my hunting rifle and have just shot them."

Then he hung up the phone again.

Within ten minutes, three police cars, a paramedic team and an ambulance roared up their street and pulled up at the Phillips' residence. A police helicopter hovered overhead. They surrounded the garden shed and caught the burglars red-handed.

One of the policemen said to George, "I thought you said that you'd shot them!"

George said, "I thought you said there was nobody available!"

Moral of the story: Don't mess with old people; they may be a jump ahead!

Note: This is allegedly a true story, but this technique would not work in parts of the world where elderly people do not normally keep hunting rifles in their homes. Increasing gun ownership and liberalising the gun laws is *not* something recommended by the Senior lobby!

Beatitudes for Seniors[26]

Blessed are they who understand

– my faltering step and palsied hand.

Blessed are they who know today

– my ears must strain for what they say.

Blessed are they who seem to know

– that my eyes are dim and my wits are slow.

Blessed are they who never say

– "You've told that story twice today."

Blessed are they who help clear away

– when coffee was spilt on the table today.

Blessed are they with cheery smile

– who stop and chat for a little while.

Blessed are they who know the way

– to bring back memories of yesterday.

---

[26] Our Sunday Visitor (1960). Permission requested.

Blessed are they who ease the days

– on my journey home in loving ways.

Twice blessed are they who make it known

– I'm loved, respected and not alone!

Amen.

Also…

Blessed are those who give without remembering

– but who take without forgetting.

Amazing Grace Cakes and Unconditional Love

David Naish served in the British Army in Normandy, helping to build bridges for the advancing allied forces in the Second World War. Then for over forty years he worked in agriculture and forestry in Balcombe, West Sussex, in the South of England. After retirement and several hip operations he slowed down, but took over the cooking at home after his wife was ill. He developed a special interest and skill in baking cakes. At some local village shows his cakes won prizes, to the chagrin of some of the local ladies!

After the death of his wife, David's faith in Jesus flourished, and he expressed this with his baking skills. His winsome method was to give away his cakes with a suitable card. When people expressed their surprise at the unsolicited free gift, "something for nothing", he had the opportunity to explain that this was the heart of the Christian message.

God's message is that we, all men and women, have made a sorry mess of things. We have, in a word, sinned and not gone in God's way.

> For everyone has sinned; we all fall short of God's glorious standard.
>
> *Romans 3:23 (NLT)*

But God took the initiative, Jesus was born in real-time history, and through his life, death and resurrection, God generously accepted that this unconditionally put things right. Eugene Peterson's translation of a passage in Paul's letter to Christians in Rome is a commentary on this. He heads it, 'God has set things right'.

> But in our time something new has been added. What Moses and the prophets witnessed to all those years ago has happened. The God-setting-things-right that we read about has become Jesus-setting-things-right for us. And not only for us, but for everyone who believes in him. For there is no difference between us and them in this. Since we've compiled this long and sorry record as sinners, both us and them, and proved that we are utterly incapable of living the glorious lives God wills for us, God did it for us. Out of sheer generosity he put us in right standing with himself. A pure gift. He got us out of the mess we're in and restored us to where he always wanted us to be. And he did it by means of Jesus Christ.
>
> *Romans 3:21-24 (The Message)*

This "sheer generosity", this "pure gift", is what we know as the "grace of God" shown in Jesus. This is the "Amazing Grace"!

> For God so loved the world that he gave his one and only Son, that whoever believes in him shall not perish but have eternal life.
>
> *John 3:16 (NIV)*

David Naish used his generosity and his cake-baking skills, developed in his retirement, to start people thinking about God's amazing grace and generosity. We did not earn it, but the free gift has paid the ransom price and set us free. What an imaginative and delicious way to share the good news of God's love!

Prayer

Dear God, thank you for taking the initiative, for your generous love shown in the life, death and resurrection of Jesus, and its meaning for each of us.

Dear God, we thank you that David Naish shows us that if we have a concern for others we can use simple domestic skills to share the message of your love.

Dear God, open our hearts with a concern for others; open our eyes to see what we can do to share your love; open our hands to make us generous with our resources and skills; and open our lips that we may speak of the Amazing Grace of Jesus.

Amen.

Pray, love and serve the poor

"If we pray,
 We will believe;
If we believe,
 We will love;
If we love,
 We will serve.
Only then can we put our love for God
Into living action
Through service of Christ
In the distressing disguise of the poor."

Mother Teresa, 1910-1997

Prayer for Seniors – Many Dimensions

Prayer is a universal human need but it is personal. It's a need to cry for help, a need to give thanks for something beautiful, a need to seek forgiveness when I've messed up, a need to reach out to someone greater, better and stronger than myself. After many years – the joys and sorrows, the elations and the disasters – now in our later years with our memories and fears, as Seniors we surely need prayer.

I'm just a pilgrim on the journey of prayer. I've been on the road most of my life, but I'm always just beginning again. Prayer is important in theory but often unsatisfactory in practice. If you find prayer a struggle, you are not alone. Mother Teresa, Billy Graham, Henri Nouwen and many paragons struggled with prayer at times. Some saints pray ecstatically for hours, and yet I tire in minutes. Prayer is a privilege, like a friendship rather than a duty, yet it requires discipline. Prayer is a place where God and human beings meet. Prayer is keeping company with God.

"Persistent prayer changes me by helping me to see the world, and my life, through God's eyes. God has a clearer picture of what I need than I do!" wrote Philip Yancey.[27]

---

[27] 'Prayer: Does it make any difference?'"; Philip Yancey; published by Hodder, London, 2006. (Hodder & Stoughton, A Division of Hodder Headline Ltd., 338 Euston Road, London NW1 3BH. www.hodderchristianbooks.co.uk.) Quotation taken from Chapter 11, 'Ask, Seek, Knock', page 143.

You can see that I aspire to prayer but am in no position to instruct anyone about it; yet I will share a few things that others have given me.

PRAYER: JESUS DID IT.

Speaking to his Father was more important for him than speaking to crowds. Jesus commanded his disciples to pray, certain that it would make a difference. But not all his prayers were answered in the way we might have expected, for example, "Take this cup from me" (Luke 22:42) or "that all of [my followers] may be one" (John 7:21). Jesus gave his disciples some instruction in prayer – The Lord's Prayer. That is useful. Think about it and pray it phrase by phrase.

Prayer is an activity, not just a good and beautiful idea; it's for doing. So don't just read about it and think about it, but do it!

LOVE GOD

The first and core principle behind prayer (and Jesus repeated it) is, love God! That is the single most important goal in life. (Matthew 22:37) It is remarkable: the sovereign God, creator and redeemer is concerned about our love. Astonishingly, he desires an ongoing relationship with each of us individuals!

Now I'm a rather simple, down-to-earth person, usually far from a 'spiritual' being, so I have questions… "Love Him with all your heart, soul and mind." – but how?

Philip Yancey, in his longest book, 'Prayer'[28] – 350 pages, with countless interviews, reviews, letters and quotations – summarises how it may be done.

"You shall love God with everything you have and everything you are. Everything. Every longing, every endowment, each of your intellectual gifts, any athletic talents or computer skill, or cooking crafts, all capacity for delight, every good thing that has your fingerprints on it – take all this, says Jesus, and refer it to God. Take your longing, and long for God; take your creaturely riches, and endow God; take your eye for beauty and appreciate God. With your heart and soul and mind, with all your needs and splendours, make a full turn towards God."

That's a big ask! But remember, being in the presence of someone you love is never a waste of time. So draw near to Him in prayer.

THE EFFECT OF PRAYERS AND THE MYSTERY OF UNANSWERED PRAYER

Philip Yancey tells of many letters from people who have written to him about disappointments with God and His response to their prayers, e.g. a crying baby who seems to cry louder when the harried mother prays for him. Others tell of unanswered prayers with more serious consequences,

---

[28] Philip Yancey; 'Prayer: Does it make any difference?'; Hodder (2006).

e.g. a child with cystic fibrosis; a mother with Alzheimer's who suddenly became violent. Philip had a file full of letters about prayers started with high hopes and dashed with disappointments. Some blame themselves; some look for positive side-effects of their prayers; others give up, concluding that prayer does not work.

Yancy's book also contains letters from those who feel they have very positive objective evidence for God's response to their prayers. For example, Gail writes:

"If I ever doubt that God hears and responds to our prayers, I pull out my prayer journal ... Reading over it I'm simply amazed at how God worked in response to my prayers ... I used to think that if I worked hard to be good enough, God would answer my prayers in the way that I wanted. Now I've learnt to bow low. I have longed for a particular result, only to realise later that it would have been disastrous. The hard times I've gone through – and there are many – have taught me that God can use anything for his purposes. I believe God often relies on us to answer the very requests we make of him."

So, the answer to prayers is sometimes a partnership. Yes, a ridiculously unbalanced partnership: God and me!

Sometimes incredible things happen. Many Christians testify to some unbelievable things that they have seen happen, and that that they believe are an answer to prayer.

Yancey puts it this way:

"I believe in miracles, but they are miracles, rare exceptions to the normal laws that govern our planet."

Years ago Archbishop William Temple said:

"When I pray coincidences happen; when I don't, they don't."[29]

MANY WAYS TO PRAY

There is a great range of ways to pray. There is a place for praying individually, or praying in a group, sometimes using words crafted with inspiration and hallowed by years of meaningful repetition, but there are so many additional, valuable and relevant ways to pray. When you read 'Aspects of Prayer for Seniors' on page 194, examine and try a few ideas. But always remember it's the 'doing it' that matters.

---

[29] Alister Hardy, 'The biology of God', page 130; Taplinger (1975). He quotes William Temple on miracles.

A Slow Motion Miracle

Emma's knee

Early in 2009 our vivacious, musical, extroverted, active and very friendly granddaughter, Emma, who lives near Lancaster, north-west England, developed acute pain in her right knee. It progressed, and by Christmas her mobility was essentially limited to a wheelchair and she had missed much school. Her medical parents, Colin and Hazel, and her grandparents wanted to give her condition a name with a clear natural history and outcome, but this was not possible. All of us, and poor Emma in particular, had to live with the uncomfortable diagnosis of "chronic pain".

After seeing many specialists in the area and having numerous painful treatments, Emma was no better, was unhappy, withdrawn and heavily medicated. The condition had been labelled "reflex sympathetic dystrophy" which has little meaning except that the nerve fibres from the knee are sending the wrong messages, which are interpreted in the brain as pain. The pain was very severe and real. Emma would become pale and perspire while waiting for the time when her next dose of pain-killer was due. Eventually, she was on Oramorph, a strong opiate analgesic, she had a fixed flexion deformity of her right leg, and we, and her parents, wondered if she would ever walk again.

In May 2010 there was a ray of hope. The "Pain team" at the famous Great Ormond Street Children's Hospital in London took her on, and there was a worldwide network praying for Emma. Her parents took unpaid leave, and the little family moved into an adjacent hospital flat. At first it was difficult to win Emma's confidence after many failed, painful treatments. With a special epidural spinal injection, specific repeated physiotherapy exercises and much prayer, her knee began to move for the first time for a year. There would be no 'quick cure' as there had been bony damage, but there was progress. Patience and persistence were necessary, but Emma's look of fear was replaced by steely determination. First the right foot touched the ground, a major milestone, then she hobbled with two crutches, then with one, then that was discarded. It took months, not weeks. It required great effort from the multi-competent Pain team, much encouragement from her parents, amazing determination from Emma and the prayers of hundreds of people. By September 2010 she started to play hockey at school and we were delighted to have our charming and cheerful granddaughter back again. We thank God and many other people who have contributed to what we believe was truly a slow-motion miracle.

In April 2013 we received an e-mail from Emma:

"On the 11th May 2013, I am doing a 10 kilometres sponsored run to raise money for 'R4TW'. I am running it with my dad. Beth and Mum are running the 5k."[30]

We thought it was wonderful that Emma used her regained mobility to help others by a sponsored run. This is something we would not have dared dream of in 2009 or 2010.

The Apostle Paul wrote to his young friend, Timothy, from prison in Rome, in about AD 66, where he awaited execution. He wrote intimately as he knew the whole family personally.

Night and day I mention you in my prayers. I am always grateful for you, as I pray to the God of my ancestors ... I also remember the genuine faith of your grandmother Lois. Your mother Eunice had the same sort of faith, and I am sure that you have it as well. So I ask you to make full use of the gift that God gave you.

2 Timothy 1:3-7 (CEV)

---

[30] Run for the World (R4TW) is a global organisation that raises awareness and funds for community development projects, through connecting organisations and groups of people so they can make a difference. Much of the money will be going towards crucial areas, such as supporting families with HIV/AIDS internationally, as well as working with children, youth and people living on the margins of society. One of the charities supported by this run is 'Ambassadors in Sport' who bring "hope through football" "to communicate the good news of Jesus Christ to all countries and people groups through football". They go into prisons, areas of great need and war zones and teach the people how to play football. While doing this, they tell people about the word of God and show them hope.

Paul pointed out how faith and blessings flowed down the generations. But we have seen that blessings do not simply flow downward in one direction in a family, from the older to the younger! We have experienced real blessing from knowing our grandchildren, and perhaps especially from Emma, as we saw her cope with a long and painful illness. Her life was a blessing to us and to many. Wonderfully she wanted to give something back through her regained mobility. May God continue to bless her and make her an inspiration! We believe that her recovery from a condition, against which medical science has limited success, is truly a miracle and an answer to prayer.

Aspects of Prayer for Seniors

Prayer may be many things. Classically it is interceding, asking God for help. It can be worship, but it can also be expressing fear, anger, insecurity and doubt. That's all right. There is a range of prayer modes, styles and aspects.

- The **quiet time prayer.**
  Prayer as a discipline, with ordered components.
- The **urgent time prayer.**
  Prayer while you or others are under stress.
- The **any time prayer.**
  Prayer while you are on the go.
- The **all the time prayer.**
  Prayer everywhere and every time.

THE QUIET TIME PRAYER

Jesus used to rise early and go off to a quiet place to spend time in prayer with his Father.

Most Seniors, unlike busy mums with several kids and a job, or a hectic CEO, can plan for some prayer time. With every stage of life your timetable will change. Be flexible, adjust, find a regular time slot that suits you, and just do it: pray.

A routine, a discipline, especially early in the day, for prayer is good. Then, how to use it? Here are some well-tried components.

- Worship, adoration and praise
Consider who God is, what He has done in creation and sustaining the earth, and what He has done for the redemption of mankind – and you and me, in particular – through the life, death and resurrection of Jesus and ongoing presence of the Holy Spirit. This is an incredible vista, a source for awe and wonder.

- Confession and asking for forgiveness
Do not compare yourself with anyone else, but honestly examine your own thoughts and performance in comparison with the primary commands of Jesus, the impossible commands to love God totally and to love even the least lovely person better than you love yourself. Remember to ask forgiveness and accept God's magnanimity.

- Thanksgiving
The two previous points provide abundant reason to give thanks. Add to these the incredible blessing that most of us receive in terms of material provision to keep us alive and loving care from family and friends.

- Intercession, prayers for others
There is huge scope and need. Many of us have lists of people and topics from our church or from organisations whose work we support. The Bible specifically asks us to pray for those in authority, for foreigners in our community and those in distress of any sort. Open your eyes to the TV or newspaper;

open your door and meet neighbours in anxiety, sorrow or loneliness. Jesus knows that we will pray for our families and close friends, but he particularly instructs us to pray for those who cheat and abuse us, our "enemies". Now that is something different, but it's His command!

- Meditation and contemplation
  In a rushed day you may feel that this is not possible, but it deserves specific consideration. (See page 206 to learn more about meditation as one method to combat anxiety.) It also has relevance to the next topic, because reading and contemplation of Bible passages is an important way that God can speak to us.

- Listening and review of our relationships with God and others
  Listening is a skill that we all need to learn and improve. It is important in communicating with others and with God. After Jesus had expounded some truths, often with a striking story, he used to say, "He who has ears, let him hear!" (or, "Are you listening to this? *Really* listening?" – Matthew 11:15, NIV and The Message) Let the life and stories of Jesus speak to our situations.

- Petition, prayers for yourself and your affairs
  Praying to God is like going to an old friend or an old Family Physician. He knows me from my youth, the ailments and accidents I have had. I don't have to repeat my whole medical or spiritual history. I

can go quickly to my current concerns. There is a danger that too much of my prayer is that of praying for myself. But Jesus said a child's approach to prayer, like asking your dad for something, was OK. (Luke 11:11-13) Sometimes the child makes foolish requests, being unaware of 'the bigger picture' and the risks of purely selfish prayers. Of course, we want God's help and blessings day by day for things great and small. But Jesus, when he prayed for himself, even in dire situations, used the caveat, "…but not what I want, but Your will be done." (Luke 22:42, CEV)

- **Commitment of yourself, your activities and contacts to God**
  At the end of your prayer time, sign off, but ask God to be with you and help you to put your prayers into action, to help you to be an answer to some of the prayers by "going out into the world to love and serve God".

THE URGENT TIME PRAYER

We all cry out in desperate times for God's help. Even Jesus did it. It is right that we do so and God expects it.

"Lord, you are a loving Father. My little grandson has meningitis. Please give the doctors and nurses the skill to diagnose and treat. Dear Lord, may the antibiotics work, may his immune system function well. He is your child. Please heal him as Jesus did when he walked the earth. Amen."

THE ANY TIME PRAYER

A young woman who came newly to faith in Jesus in her twenties was asking an older Christian friend about how, when and where to pray. As it was explained to her that God was always open and eager to hear her prayers she had a 'wow moment'.

"You mean I don't have to be in church, but wherever I am and whatever I'm doing, I can speak to God? That is an amazing, open-access friendship privilege!"

And it is! Let us not forget it.

In addition to having a set 'quiet time', it is useful to fit prayer into many of the activities of your day. Sometimes I relate my short prayers to what I am doing.

"Lord, I'm scrubbing away in this shower, but please do the real cleansing from my bad thoughts and ways."

"Lord, I'm thirsty and this cup of tea is great, but please make me thirst for you and satisfy me with your 'water of life'!"

Pray when you are walking the dog, doing your exercises, standing at the bus stop or at the kitchen sink or in the check-out line, or waiting for the computer to power up.

Note, however, that 'any time' prayer is not good when driving in traffic or doing other things that demand concentration. That's a disservice to God and a danger to everyone!

THE ALL THE TIME PRAYER

Prayer is less a technique than a relationship. It is keeping conscious company with God. Saying prayers is an activity, but praying through life is more of an attitude, a way in which you face life's duties, problems and pleasures as you live your life 24/7.

So, make prayer a part of life, of what you do; as you paint or write, shop or cook, make music or garden, visit the doctor or climb a hill. Let everything you attempt be done with and for God. Not easy, but a good objective!

Brother Lawrence (1614-1691), born Nicolas Herman, lived in Lorraine, in eastern France. For some time he was a soldier but felt called by a revelation to a religious life, and served in a priory in Paris. Lacking much education to be a cleric, he spent most of his life working in the kitchen or repairing sandals. Despite his lowly position in life, his character attracted many to him. He had a reputation for experiencing profound peace, and visitors came to seek spiritual guidance. The wisdom he passed on in conversations and in letters became the basis for the book 'The Practice of the Presence of God'.

Brother Lawrence felt that he cooked meals, ran errands, scrubbed pots, and endured the scorn of the world alongside God. One of his most famous sayings refers to his kitchen:

"The time of business does not with me differ from the time of prayer; and in the noise and clatter of my kitchen, while several persons are at the same time calling for different things, I possess God in as great tranquillity as if I were upon my knees before the Blessed Sacrament."

Additional Prayers for Seniors

Accepting dependence

O Lord my God, grant me the grace to accept the realities of life. Lord, help me to accept my various failings:

- My physical and mental failings, which make me more dependent on the care and mercy of others.
- My temperamental and spiritual failings, which make me more dependent on the tolerance of others and completely dependent on your grace and mercy.
- My weakness. I am not strong enough to change many things, but make me strong enough to change the way I think. Make me positive about my circumstances.

Lord, as I accept things, remove bitterness and give me gratitude and love in my heart.

Lord, I look back with thanks for the love, care and nurture I received from my mother when I was a baby, small, helpless and completely dependent.

Lord, I look back with gratitude for the busy years when I was more independent, had strength, skills and energy to care for and help others.

Lord, I look around with gratitude for the care and love that is shown to me now, now that I cannot do everything for myself and I cannot do much for others.

Lord, teach me gently the lessons of dependence.

Lord, I await with trepidation the time when I may be completely dependent on others for my simple physical needs. Give me acceptance of my helplessness. Give me gentle carers and the mind and heart to express my thanks.

Lord, I look forward with expectancy to the time when I will be free of the limitations of my ageing body and mind and will be free to devote myself to worship and serve you completely.

Lord Jesus,

- the power of God was at your disposal but you accepted weakness;
- the army of heaven was at your command but you chose obedience;
- at your trial your word would have reversed the verdict, but you chose to say, "Not my will, but Yours."

Lord Jesus, teach me to be obedient to your will and to cast myself on your loving care today and always.

Amen.

The nun's prayer

Dear Lord, you know, better than I know myself, that I am older than I imagine. In fact I am really quite old!

With my vast store of wisdom it seems a pity not to use it all, but you know, Lord, that I want a few friends at the end. Keep me from being too talkative and particularly from the habit of thinking I must say something on every subject and on every occasion. Release me from the craving to try and straighten out everybody's affairs.

When it is my opportunity to speak, keep me from repetition and the recital of old stories or endless details. Give me wings to get to the point. Make me thoughtful but not moody, helpful but not bossy.

I ask for grace to listen to the tales of others, pains. Help me to endure them, for the narration brings some relief to them.

Seal my lips about my many aches and pains. They are increasing and my love of rehearsing them becomes sweeter as the years go by.

I dare not ask for improved memory but for growing humility and less cocksureness when my memory seems to clash with the memory of others. Teach me, merciful Lord, the glorious lesson that occasionally I may be mistaken.

Good Lord, keep me reasonably sweet. I do not want to be a saint – some of them are hard to live with – but a grumpy old man or a sour old woman are crowning works of the devil.

Give me the ability to see good things in unexpected places, and talents in unexpected people. Give me, O Lord, the grace to praise and encourage them. Help me still to extract all possible fun out of life. May my preoccupation with self not blind me to the many funny things around, Lord; keep me perceptive to the comic.

O Lord, many of my senses are failing, but kindly sustain my sense of humour!

Amen.

Variations on a Famous Prayer[31]

The serenity prayer

Good Lord, grant me
the serenity to accept the things I cannot change,
the courage to change the things I can,
and the wisdom to know the difference.

Reinhold Niebuhr

The senility prayer

Good Lord, grant me
the senility to forget the people I never liked,
the good fortune to meet up with the ones I do like,
and the eyesight to see the difference.

Anon

More prayers for the older generation are available in the booklet 'William Barclay's Prayers for Seniors'[32]. These include prayers for some specific situations which are relevant to Seniors: for example 'accepting dependence', which is shown above.

---

[31] Remember that Jesus had a sense of humour! "You hypocrite! First take the log out of your own eye, and then you will be able to see clearly to take the speck out of your friend's eye." (Matthew 7:5, NIV)
[32] St. Paul's Press, Mumbai (2008); ISBN 978-81-7109-886-8. Or in UK from William Cutting: *william.cutting@talktalk.net*

When Seniors Pray…

Texas beer joint sues church over lightning strike

The above headline is from a local newspaper. The following story is alleged to be true.

Drummond's Bar began construction on expansion of their building to increase their business. In response, the local Baptist Church started a campaign to block the bar from expanding, with petitions and prayers. Work progressed right up until the week before the grand reopening, when lightning struck the bar and it burned to the ground!

After the bar burning to the ground by the lightning strike, the church folk were rather smug, bragging about "the power of prayer"… until the bar owner sued the church on the grounds that the church "was ultimately responsible for the destruction of his building and business, either through direct or indirect actions or means".

In its reply to the court, the church vehemently denied all responsibility or any connection to the building's demise.

The judge read through the plaintiff's complaint and the defendant's reply, and at the opening hearing he commented, "I don't know how I'm going to decide this, but it appears from the paperwork that we have a bar owner who believes in the power of prayer, and an entire church congregation that denies the power of prayer."

Meditate – a Christian Alternative to Worry

David, the shepherd boy who became a poet and a great King, was quite a worrier.

> Rescue me from the mire, do not let me sink; deliver me from those who hate me, from the deep waters. Do not let the floodwaters engulf me or the depths swallow me up or the pit close its mouth over me.
>
> *Psalm 69:14-15 (NIV)*

> I cry aloud to the Lord; I lift up my voice to the Lord for mercy. I pour out my complaint before him; before him I tell my trouble. When my spirit grows faint within me, it is you who know my way. In the path where I walk men have hidden a snare for me. Look to my right and see; no one is concerned for me.
>
> *Psalm 142:1-4*

But David had a solution: **meditation – on God's word.**

Blessed is the man who does not walk in the counsel of the wicked or stand in the way of sinners or sit in the seat of mockers. But his delight is in the law of the Lord, and on His law he meditates day and night.

Psalm 1:1-2

John Fischer wrote this:[33]

"I'm a chronic worrier and I'm good at it. I come from a long line of worriers. A good deal of my conscious time is taken up with worrying."

Worry is focused thinking. It's focused on what I can't answer or solve about my situation. Worry, at least for me, is returning over and over again to a place where I am stuck. I must somehow negatively feed on that little flutter of panic each time I follow a path of worry to the same hopeless conclusion. These are thoughts that accompany me throughout the day. Worry is nagging negativity.

Meditation is also focused thinking.

It is not just for monks and clerics. It is not only the alternative but also the antidote to worry. David said that he loved to meditate day and night on the word of God. Now this was also while he was busy, running a kingdom, fighting a perpetual enemy on the battlefield, and at times, fleeing for his life. He didn't have a lot of time to sit with his legs crossed and go "Ommmmmm..." That kind of meditation is meant to clear or even empty the mind of all thoughts. Biblical meditation is thinking focused on a particular aspect of God, a part of God's word, or a reminder of what He has done for you.

If, as an expert, I can worry during my work and leisure, then I could choose to meditate on God's word instead. Worry is usually all about what you can't do

---

[33] www.catchjohnfischer.wordpress.com. Used by permission.

anything about. It's never productive. If I learned to turn my chronic worrying into meditation, all that time and attention could be turned to God and his truth. Then, when I sit down to do something about those worries, I might be better able to find a solution!

Go away! It's hard enough arranging my arthritis meditatively without an audience.

Try it today. If you catch yourself worrying, turn your thoughts instead to God and his word.

Take a portion of scripture and turn it over and over in your mind. Repeat it; think of its meaning; take it into your heart. Remember what God has done for you. Be thankful.

Why worry when you can meditate?

David's Psalms and the words of Jesus give many verses to focus on. Here are a few, but there are many more for you to find and make your own.

Praise the Lord, O my soul; all my inmost being, praise his holy name. Praise the Lord, O my soul, and forget not all his benefits...

Psalm 103:1-2 (NIV)

The Lord is a refuge for the oppressed, a stronghold in times of trouble.

Psalm 9:9 (NIV)

The LORD is my shepherd; I have all that I need.

Psalm 23:1 (GNT)

The Lord is my light and my salvation; whom shall I fear? The Lord is the strength of my life; of whom shall I be afraid?

Psalm 27:1 (NIV)

The Lord will fulfil his purpose for me; your love, O Lord, endures for ever.

Psalm 138:8 (TLB)

[Jesus said,] "God blesses those people who depend only on him. They belong to the kingdom of heaven!"

Matthew 5:3 (CEV)

[Jesus said,] "I tell you not to worry about your life. Don't worry about having something to eat, drink, or wear. Isn't life more than food or clothing?"

Matthew 6:25 (CEV)

[Jesus said,] "I am the way, the truth, and the life! Without me, no one can go to the Father."

John 14:6 (CEV)

[Jesus said,] "I give you peace, the kind of peace that only I can give. It isn't like the peace that this world can give. So don't be worried or afraid."

John 12:27 (CEV)

Here is an ancient and simple prayer that has been used for centuries for meditation:[34]

"Lord Jesus Christ, have mercy on me."

It acknowledges the supremacy and lordship of Jesus Christ. It declares that I am in need of redemption and this is found in Christ alone.

---

[34] See 'The Way of the Pilgrim', translated from the Russian by R.M French; 1965.

Three o'clock in the Morning

At three in the morning I used to be sleeping
   an untroubled sleep in my bed.
But lately at three in the morning
   I'm tossing and turning,
Awakened by hypochondria, and gas,
   and nameless dread,
Whose name I've been learning... WORRY.

At three in the morning I brood about what
   my cholesterol count might reveal,
And the pains in my chest start
   progressing from gentle to racking,
While certain intestinal problems make clear that
   the onions I ate with my meal
Plan on counter attacking.

At three in the morning I look toward the future
   with blankets pulled over my ears,
And all of my basic equipment
   is distinctly diminished.
My gums are receding, my blood pressure's high,
   and I can't begin listing my fears
Or I'll never get finished.

At three in the morning I used to be sleeping
    but lately I wake and reflect
That my girlhood's long gone
    and I'll now have to manage without it.
They tell me that I'm heading into my prime.
    From the previews I do not expect
To be crazy about it.

Judith Viorst [35]

Sleepless? Worried?
Don't count sheep, but speak to the Shepherd.

---

[35] Judith is an American, born in 1931, a journalist, psychoanalysis researcher and author, especially of children's books and poems that reflect on love, marriage and the passing of years.

Seniors should Look Upward

Bible verses in contemporary language for this part of the journey

WAKE UP!

Decide to have a good day.

This day belongs to the LORD! Let's celebrate and be glad today.

Psalm 118:24 (CEV)

DRESS UP!

Put on a smile; it's inexpensive and improves your looks. But remember...

...the LORD told Samuel, ... "People judge others by what they look like, but I judge people by what is in their hearts."

1 Samuel 16:7 (CEV)

SPEAK UP!

Say true things, but with love.

God wants us to grow up, to know the whole truth and tell it in love – like Christ in everything.

Ephesians 4:15 (The Message)

Careful words make for a careful life; careless talk may ruin everything.

Proverbs 13:3 (The Message)

SHUT UP!

Learn to listen. God gave us two ears and one mouth. Listen more; talk less.

> And Jesus concluded, "Listen, then, if you have ears!"
>
> *Mark 4:9 (GNT)*

STAND UP!

Stand for what is true and good, or you will fall for anything.

> So then, our friends, stand firm and hold on to those truths which we taught you.
>
> *2 Thessalonians 2:15 (GNT)*

WORK UP!

Everyone can work better, whether the job is big or small.

> Good planning and hard work lead to prosperity, but hasty shortcuts lead to poverty.
>
> *Proverbs 21:5 (NLT)*

> Work with enthusiasm, as though you were working for the Lord rather than for people.
>
> *Ephesians 6:7 (NLT)*

> Don't get tired of helping others. You will be rewarded when the time is right, if you don't give up.
>
> *Galatians 6:9-10 (CEV)*

CHEER UP AND COUGH UP!

Knowing God and giving are the secrets of joy.

Always be full of joy in the Lord. I say it again – rejoice. Let everyone see that you are considerate in all you do.

Philippians 4:4-5 (NLT)

Each of you must make up your own mind about how much to give. But don't feel sorry that you must give and don't feel that you are forced to give. God loves people who love to give.

2 Corinthians 9:7 (CEV)

LOOK UP!

Look to the Lord, not just your own strength.

Christ gives me the strength to face anything.

Philippians 4:13 (CEV)

REACH UP!

Reach for something higher, full commitment.

Trust in the LORD with all your heart; do not depend on your own understanding. Seek his will in all you do, and he will show you which path to take.

Proverbs 3:5-6 (NLT)

LIFT UP!

Lift up your prayers.

Don't worry about anything; instead, pray about everything. Tell God what you need, and thank him for all he has done.

Philippians 4:6 (NLT)

The up word and the infuriating English language

There is one word that can be a noun, verb, adjective, adverb, and preposition:

It is up.

This two-letter English word has more meanings than any other two-letter word.

It's easy to understand up meaning 'toward the sky' or 'at the top of the list', but when we awaken in the morning, why do we wake up?

At a meeting, why does a topic come up? Why do we speak up, and why is it that officers are up for election but if there is a tie it is a toss up or you divide up the job?

Why is it up to the secretary to write up a report?

We call up our friends, brighten up a room, polish up the silver, warm up the leftovers and clean up the kitchen. We lock up the house and fix up the old bicycle.

People stir up trouble, queue up (line up) for tickets, work up an appetite, and think up excuses.

At other times, this little word has really special meaning. To be dressed is one thing, but to be dressed up is special.

To cheer myself up
I was all dressed up
But found I'd slipped up
When the storm blew up
No brolly to put up.

And this **up** is confusing. A drain must be opened up because it is stopped up. We open up a door in the morning but we close it up at night. We seem to be pretty mixed up about up!

To be knowledgeable about the proper uses of up, look up the word up in the dictionary. In a desk-sized dictionary, it takes up almost a whole page and can add up to about thirty definitions.

If you feel up to it, you might try building up a list of the many ways up is used. It will take up a lot of your time, but if you don't give up, you may wind up with up to a hundred or more.

It crops up in weather reports. When it threatens to rain, we say it is clouding up. When the sun comes out, we say it is clearing up. When it rains, the earth soaks it up. When it does not rain for a while, things dry up.

One could go on and on, but I'll wrap it up for now as my time is up!

Oh... one more thing: What is the last thing you do at night and the first thing you do in the morning? Using these two little letters: U P! Except of course if you are a true Senior; then the night is disturbed several times because you have to get **up.**

Did that one crack you up?

Or do you suspect that I have cracked up?

Don't worry, now I'll shut up!

Jesus Loves Me

Testimonies from a Senior Pastor and a great theologian

What follows is a report from a Senior in USA.

Recovering from my knee replacement I was not able to go to church last Sunday. I watched a service in a church in Atlanta, Georgia. In the service they were honouring one of its Senior Pastors who had been retired many years. He was ninety-two at that time and I wondered why the church even bothered to ask the old gentleman to speak at that age?

After a warm welcome, and the applause quieted down, he rose from his high back chair and walked slowly and stiffly, with great effort and a sliding gait to the desk. Without a note or written paper of any kind he placed both hands on the pulpit to steady himself and then slowly but gently and firmly he began to speak.

"When I was asked to come here today and talk to you, your pastor asked me to tell you what was the greatest lesson I ever learned in my fifty-odd years of preaching. I thought about it for a few days and boiled it down to just one thing, the thing that made the most difference in my life and sustained me through all my trials; the one thing that I could always rely on when problems rose up, when heartbreak and tears poured down, or when pain and fear and sorrow paralyzed me. The only thing that would comfort and strengthen was this verse. And it is a verse for us all!

"Jesus loves me, this I know,
For the Bible tells me so.
Little ones to Him belong,
We are weak but He is strong.

"Yes, Jesus loves me,
Yes, Jesus loves me,
Yes, Jesus loves me,
The Bible tells me so."

When he finished, the church was quiet. You could actually hear his every foot step as he shuffled back to his chair. I don't believe I will ever forget it. I don't think that any of those who heard his simple testimony will ever forget it.

Karl Barth, the Swiss theologian (1886-1968), possibly the greatest Protestant Christian scholar of the Twentieth Century, wrote many volumes about the Christian faith. He was asked to summarise his personal belief in a sentence and he quoted the first two lines of the song:

Jesus loves me, this I know,
For the Bible tells me so.

The core of the Christian message is in two lines of a children's hymn!

A pastor once stated:

"I always noticed that it was the adults who chose the children's hymn 'Jesus Loves Me' – for the children, of course. During the hymn singing it was the adults who sang the loudest because I could see they knew it the best."

These lyrics originally appeared as a poem by Anna B. Warner (1827-1915) in the context of a novel called 'Say and Seal', written by her sister Susan Warner and published in 1860. Their father was a New York Lawyer who lost his money in a depression, and the girls took up teaching and writing. The tune usually used with the song was added in 1862 by William B. Bradbury.

Jesus Loves Me – Senior version

Jesus loves me, this I know,
For the Bible tells me so.
People all to Him belong,
They are weak, but He is strong.

Chorus:
Yes, Jesus loves me. Yes, Jesus loves me.
Yes, Jesus loves me. The Bible tells me so.

Jesus loves me, this I know,
Though my hair is white as snow,
Though my sight is growing dim,
Still He tells me, trust in Him.

Though my steps are now more slow,
With my hand in His I'll go.
On through life, let come what may,
He'll be there to lead the way.

Though I am no longer young,
I have much which He's begun.
Though my mind is now more slow,
In my spirit I still grow.

When the nights are dark and long,
In my heart He puts a song.
Telling me in words so clear,
Have no fear for I am near.

When my work on earth is done,
And life's victories have been won.
He will take me home above,
Then I'll understand His love.

I love Jesus, does he know?
Have I ever told him so?
Jesus loves to hear me say
That I love Him every day.

Choirs, Human and Angelic

Singing in a choir can be one of life's greatest experiences. Being a member of a team that makes music using voices in harmony seems to satisfy, empower and encourage more effectively than many other experiences in life.

This has recently been demonstrated by a charismatic choir leader in Britain, Gareth Malone. An important choir project was with a group of wives and girlfriends of British soldiers serving in Afghanistan. As a group these women felt isolated, shunned by the general public, many of whom opposed military intervention there. They lived in a state of constant tension and fear about the next fatality or injury report from the frontline. Gareth mobilised the women, most of whom had never sung in a choir before, and used the words from love letters exchanged with their separated partners.

"Wherever you are, my heart will keep you safe."[36]

After the choir appeared on TV and sang before the Queen and Prime Minister at the Remembrance Day celebration in the Royal Albert Hall in November 2011, their song soared in popularity to become the coveted Number 1 single before Christmas 2011. The transformation in the group of women was dramatic; from reclusive and fearful they became dynamic, bringing their plight and courage to

---

[36] 'Wherever you are' by the Military wives. Music by Paul Mealor.

the attention of many. "That is the power of music and singing together," said Gareth.

Hallelujah!

Singing can also enliven Seniors. In 2008 a British documentary entitled 'Young at Heart'[37] captured a choir in New England, USA, with an average age of eighty. In preparation for a concert in their home town they spent two months learning a wide range of new material. The film is full of humour and poignant moments, and the choir's determination to succeed increased with the sudden deaths of two of the members. During training this remarkable group held a concert at a prison. The deeply moving performance concludes with the singers walking into the audience, greeting the surprised prisoners with handshakes and hugs.

---

[37] 'Young at heart' DVD by 20th Century Fox, available from Amazon etc.

The film won a number of awards and even grossed nearly $4 million at the box office. More important, the singing, camaraderie and a sense of fun lifted these Seniors to unexpected heights. Once again, we see the power of music and singing.

For two thousand years Christians have praised God and shared their faith in song. Virtually every branch of Christ's Church has stated the truths of the faith and encouraged each other in song. At the first Christmas, an angel announced the birth of Jesus to a group of shepherds in the open air and...

> ...at once the angel was joined by a huge angelic choir singing God's praises: Glory to God in the heavenly heights, peace to all men and women on earth...
>
> *Luke 2:13-14 (The Message)*

Never before, or since, has such a humble audience enjoyed such a spectacular choral concert. But it was the most important birthday of all time, so it deserved something more special than the routine "Happy birthday to you!"

The Senior choir in New England transformed the life of the Seniors there. Singing should be on the agenda of all Seniors' groups!

Singing is particularly appropriate for the big festivals of the year: Christmas and Easter.

Where do Christmas songs begin?
By the stable of an inn
where the songs of hosts on high
mingled with a baby's cry.
There for joy and wonder smiled
man and maid and holy child.
    Christmas songs begin with them:
    Sing the songs of Bethlehem![38]

Timothy Dudley-Smith (1926)
English hymn writer and a retired bishop

---

[38] 'Where do Christmas songs begin?' by Timothy Dudley-Smith (b. 1926). © Timothy Dudley-Smith in Europe and Africa. © Hope Publishing Company in the United States of America and the rest of the world. First verse reproduced by permission of Oxford University Press. All rights reserved.

What is Christ?

The Shield from every dart;
The Balm for every smart;
The Sharer of each load;
Companion on the road –
 is Jesus!

The Door into the fold;
The Anchor that will hold;
The Shepherd of the sheep;
The Guardian of my sleep –
 is Jesus!

The Friend with whom I talk;
The Way by which I walk;
The Light to show the way;
The Strength for every day -
 is Jesus!

The Source of my delight;
The Song to cheer the night;
The Thought that fills my mind;
The Best of All to find –
 is Jesus!

Anonymous

St. Patrick's Breastplate

Christ Be Near at Either Hand[39]

Christ be near at either hand,
Christ behind, before me stand,
Christ around, above, below.
Christ with me where e'er I go,

Christ be in my heart and mind,
Christ within my soul enshrined,
Christ control my wayward heart,
Christ abide and ne'er depart.

Christ my life and only way,
Christ my light by night and day,
Christ my true, unchanging friend,
Guide and shepherd to the end.

---

[39] This hymn, written by the Irish Catholic Priest, Fr. John Fennelly
(1890-1966) is based on excerpts from 'St. Patrick's Breastplate',
attributed to Saint Patrick in the 5th century.

Contact the Author

The author would be happy to receive comments or
communications about this book or series at:

william.cutting@talktalk.net

Also by the Author

Face the Future book 1
Seniors Can Inspire, Apply Wisdom and Model Values
FOREWORD BY FIONA CASTLE

The first book in the Face the Future series demonstrates how Seniors can make a positive change in society. Whether it is helping other Seniors or inspiring the younger generation, whether it is challenging the policies of global organisations or helping to protect the environment, Seniors have a wealth of wisdom and wit to draw upon. Inspiring examples are given of Seniors who have impacted politics, the media and other fields. But active Seniors also recognise that there is always more to learn – and do so...

Available from www.onwardsandupards.org